THE ALAN TURING
CODEBREAKER'S
PUZZLE BOOK

THE ALAN TURING
CODEBREAKER'S PUZZLE BOOK

Compiled by Dr Gareth Moore

Foreword by
Sir Dermot Turing

ARCTURUS

ARCTURUS

This edition published in 2019 by Arcturus Publishing Limited
26/27 Bickels Yard, 151–153 Bermondsey Street,
London SE1 3HA

Copyright © Arcturus Holdings Limited
Compiled by Any Puzzle Media Ltd

The Turing Trust logo © The Turing Trust

ISBN: 978-1-78950-378-4
AD007166UK

Printed in China

Contents

FOREWORD

Alan Turing's last published paper was about puzzles. It was written for the popular science magazine *Penguin Science News*, and its theme was to explain to the general reader that while many mathematical problems will be solvable, it is not possible ahead of time to know whether any particular problem will be solvable or not. He illustrates his point using various homely things such as a tangled knot of string, and the sliding-squares puzzle where you have to restore the pattern by moving squares into an empty space. So, and with neat symmetry, Alan Turing's last paper covers the same subject as his first, in which – as well as dealing with provability testing for mathematical theorems – he set out what is now regarded as a blueprint for a programmable computer.

Alan Turing's role in the development of computers in the mid-twentieth century is well known, as is his work at Bletchley Park in disentangling one of the most strategically important puzzles of World War II, the Enigma cipher machine. The Enigma machine used a different cipher for every letter in a message; the only way to decipher a message was to know how the machine had been set up at the start of encryption, and then to follow the mechanical process of the machine. The codebreakers had to find this out, and the answer was not in the back of the book. Although they did not have computers to help them, with Alan Turing's aid, new electrical and electronic devices were invented which sifted out impossible and unlikely combinations and so reduced the puzzle to a manageable size. And the experience with these new machines laid the foundation for the development of electronic digital computers in the post-war years.

Computers are now commonplace, not only in the workplace and on a desk at home, in a smartphone or tablet, but in almost every piece of modern machinery. Teaching people computer skills and coding are now considered obvious elements of the curriculum. Except that this is not so, in all parts of the world. In Africa, access to computers is extremely variable, and in some countries there is little or no opportunity for students to have hands-on experience of a real computer. For example, in 2017, only 6 per cent of Malawian households owned a computer.

The Turing Trust, a charity founded by Alan Turing's great-nephew James in 2009, aims to confront these challenges in a practical way which pays homage to Alan Turing's legacy in computer development. The Turing Trust provides still-working, used computers to African schools, enabling computer labs to be built in rural areas where students would otherwise be taught about computers with blackboard and chalk. The computers are refurbished and provided with an e-library of resources relevant to the local curriculum, and then sent out to give a new purpose and bring opportunity to underprivileged communities.

Thank you for buying this book and supporting the Turing Trust.

Sir Dermot Turing
July 2019

To find out more, visit *www.turingtrust.co.uk*

Introduction

About the Puzzles

The puzzles in this book are different from those you will typically come across elsewhere. Instead of being told exactly what to do, here part of the challenge is to work out the rules of each puzzle for yourself. That doesn't mean you have to guess, but rather you need to tease out how to solve each one from the hints that are hidden on the page.

Every puzzle in this book has both a number and a title. The number is simply for cross-referencing with the hints and solutions, but the title can be important – incredibly important, in some cases, where it may be the only hint you get as to what to do.

The puzzles are extremely varied, but there are inevitably some repeated mechanics, such as anagrams, or inserted or deleted letters. As you work your way through the book you should find your puzzle-solving skills gradually improving.

Puzzle Difficulty

There are five chapters of puzzles, and – as hinted at by the chapter titles– they become progressively more difficult. Depending on your experience you may be able to dive right into the final chapter, but if you fancy a gentler introduction then it's probably best to start with the first chapter, at least until you get into the flow of it.

It doesn't matter what order you solve the puzzles in – so you can jump around as you please. If you don't see how to get started on a puzzle, why not leave it for another time and try the next one instead?

Hints

When you get stuck – and you will definitely get stuck at some point – there are three things you can do. First, you can take a break, or chat it over with someone else who might have a fresh point of view or idea. Second, you can take a look at the solutions – which work on a step-by-step basis, so reading just a bit of a solution can be a fair method to get you started for some puzzles, without giving the entire game away. Or third, you can turn to the special hints section, in the middle of the book.

Each hint is broken down into a number of bulleted points – some puzzles have lots of points, while occasionally a puzzle has only one. The points become more and more specific the more you read, so reading the first hint will usually give you only a gentle nudge in the direction of what to do. Further hints become progressively more specific, until in some cases you are told how to go about solving the puzzle – but you are never given the full answer. For that you will need the solutions.

Solutions

The solutions provide two things. First, they do give you the answer to the question as asked, if indeed a question *was* asked – some puzzles simply present content without comment, and it is up to you to work out what is being asked of you! But second, and perhaps more importantly, they show you exactly how you reach that answer, explaining each part of the puzzle in a step-by-step way. This means that even if you initially find the puzzles hard to fathom, if you read through the solutions then you should start to understand how they work.

Twisted Minds

The puzzles in this book come from the minds of more than ten different authors, most of whom have considerable experience in setting devious and cryptic challenges, as you can see from their biographies at the back of the book. Sometimes different authors will approach similar puzzle mechanics from very different angles, making sure you are kept on your toes!

Good luck – and have fun!

Gareth Moore, July 2019

Chapter 1

Decipherable

Alan Turing worked on many different projects throughout his life, with perhaps his most famous legacies being the invention of the Turing Machine, the Turing Test and of course his critical codebreaking work during World War II. Luckily, the puzzles in this chapter are considerably easier to crack than the challenges Turing faced during the War, but, even so, you will still find some challenging enigmas on the pages that follow.

① FLOWER POWER

In what way can the following sentences be said to contain flowery language?

- ▶ A sparkling diamond for the debonair is the height of fashion

- ▶ Skilled jewel-cutters shape onyx with tools

- ▶ Lapis lazuli lack the wide range of hues found in other jewels

- ▶ Euros enable the purchase of German garnets

- ▶ A gem-buying agenda is yielding high profits

② MOVIE EDITS

The following short phrases each represent a well-known film title. Work out how, and then reveal them all.

- ▶ Oh, fat true bucket!

- ▶ Wed? Nothing white

- ▶ Chill 'n distress

- ▶ Angry, invasive trap

- ▶ Performs gut

③ WORD CONNECTIONS

There are three words missing in the diagram below. Can you complete it so that all pairs of touching words form a word when joined together?

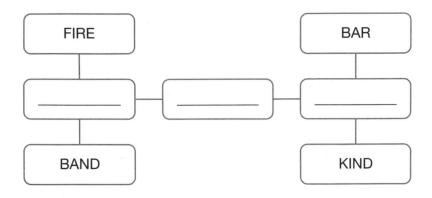

(4) END OF SERIES

What is the final letter in this series?

▶ T S E L R N S

(5) WHAT THE...?

The following characters have all been manipulated in the same way. Given the same treatment, what would the author's name look like?

▶ Llts

▶ Srggj

▶ Skrb

▶ Tswt

▶ Kcwkcp

▶ Hctwgm

⑥ CLOCK SCHEDULING

Given the following, what time would Loos represent?

▸ Britain = twenty to eight in the evening

▸ Waterloo = quarter past six in the evening

▸ Berlin = quarter to eight in the evening

▸ Loos = _____

⑦ COMPLETE THE PICTURE

What is missing from each entry?

▸ D_____ USA

▸ N_____ Nigeria

▸ B_____ India

▸ H_____ USA

⑧ PUNAGRAMS I

Solve the anagrams below to reveal six European countries. However, each anagram has one extra letter that isn't used. In order, these read to give an answer to this question:

Which European country do athletes dislike?

▶ BIG MULES   _____   —

▶ PURE SLAB   _____ _____   —

▶ LINED CAR   _____ _____   —

▶ OVEN ALIAS   _____ _____   —

▶ NEW SIDE   _____.   —

▶ RRAISEN   __ _____   —

⑨ TETRA-DROP GRID FILL

Drop the tetromino pieces into the grid in the order given so as to spell out ten six-letter words. The pieces may not be rotated or reflected, and must be able to be dropped into the grid from the top so that they come to rest on either another piece or the grid bottom.

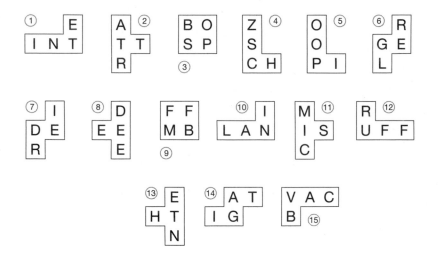

(10) QUOTE HANJIE

Shade in squares in the grid to reveal a quote. Numbers at the start of each row or column reveal, in order from left to right or top to bottom, the length of each consecutive run of shaded squares. There must be a gap of at least one empty square between each run of shaded squares in the same row or column.

Once you have identified and shaded all of the correct squares, the remaining letters will spell out an inspiring quote from Alan Turing.

			2 1 3	1	2 1 1	1 6	2 2 2	1 1 2	1 1 1	1	2 1 1
1	2	1	Y	T	E	O	H	O	S	E	T
1	1	1	E	W	S	H	O	C	A	N	P
		2	I	M	A	R	A	G	I	N	E
3	1	1	A	N	E	N	T	Y	B	T	O
	1	1	U	H	I	H	N	G	C	A	N
		3	C	R	E	C	N	U	A	T	E
1	2	3	H	T	H	A	T	E	C	O	L
1	1	1	O	I	M	H	P	L	O	S	S
	3	2	V	A	S	I	B	A	D	L	E

(11) ANAGRAM CONNECTIONS I

Unscramble the following words and find a word that connects them. Note that although some words have more than one anagram, only one of these will fit the connecting word.

- ▶ CORNLOT

- ▶ ROVE

- ▶ DUFN

- ▶ NI

- ▶ ELAPSING

- ▶ COURSE

- ▶ FIGURNS

- ▶ TI

- ▶ DINGDAM

Solve the anagrams below to reveal seven chemical elements. However, each anagram has one extra letter that isn't used. In order, these read to give an answer to this question:

What is a doctor's most-preferred element?

▶ CHOPPER   _____   __

▶ ORANGE   __ _____   __

▶ COIN SAIL   ____ _____ _   __

▶ IS MOULD   _____   __

▶ EVIL SIR   _____ ___ __   __

▶ UNIT   _____   __

▶ MEDAL   _____   __

(13) COMMON FEATURES I

What is the common feature of all of these words and phrases?

- ▸ Choice key
- ▸ Tall kebabs
- ▸ North tail
- ▸ Nine battles
- ▸ Hear cry
- ▸ A mint bond

(14) ODD NAME OUT I

Which of Oscar's friends is the odd one out?

- ▸ Gigi
- ▸ Hugo
- ▸ Marty
- ▸ Oliver
- ▸ Rebecca

⑮ THE VAULT

Mentally revolve the two inner disks until eight four-letter words are lined up. Each word will begin with the central E and read outwards in a radial line.

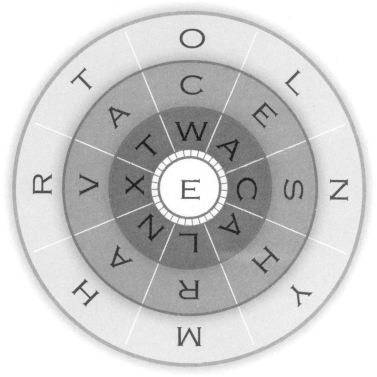

What do all of the following represent, and what property connects them?

- SESESESESESESESESESE
- OILLIS

-   M
  TANA
- PRIME HASH

- AINIGRIV
- I CUT

(17) COMMON FEATURES 2

Can you derive a common language feature of all of
these words? What is your reference? Where are you
coming from?

▶ Moped

▶ Ombudsman

▶ Orienteering

▶ Tungsten

(18) WATCH THIS

Complete the following calculation:
(Ronin − Days Later) × Angry Men − Hours = _____

(19) ALTERNATIVE EXPRESSIONS

Can you re-express each of these phrases?

▸ A palm's robin has double the value of a shrub robin

▸ A destiny worse than an ending

▸ Well known for 900 seconds

▸ A sharp pain in the side, that's punctual, rescues just under ten

▸ Tear up because lactose has pooled on the floor

▸ Trout on land

ANAGRAM CONNECTIONS 2

Unscramble the following words and find a word
that connects them. Note that although some words
have more than one anagram, only one will fit the
connecting word.

▸ TREAF

▸ AKTECJ

▸ GHHI

▸ ITEM

▸ FALH

▸ DISZE

▸ DOBOL

▸ LAYFIM

▸ CLEYC

▸ DARGU

㉑ SIX MIX

There are six anagrammable words of six letters each in the first of the following grids. A seventh word, LAPTOP, can be read in the marked diagonal.

Rearrange the six words into six new words, and place them into the second grid in such a way that the word PURPLE occupies the diagonal shaded squares.

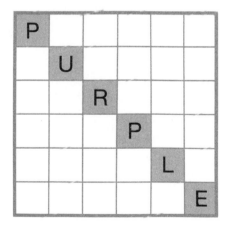

㉒ KEY NUMBERS

If !)) is a ton, ((is a type of ice cream, !*!% is Waterloo,))& is a fictional spy and ^^^ is satanic, what would (!! mean, in the US?

㉓ CONNECTION

What connects the following items?

▶ Cafetière

▶ Salad accompaniment

▶ Unauthorized absence

▶ Eggy bread

▶ Fried Potatoes

(24) LITERARY SET

Can you identify what category of things is being referenced in the same way in the following titles of literary works?

▸ The Murder Road

▸ H is for Kettle

▸ The Parliament and the Pussycat

▸ The Maltese Cast

▸ The Wings of the Flight

▸ Where Convocations Dare

▸ Wild Bevies

▸ Flaubert's Company

▸ Shroud for a Watch

25 MOVIE CLUB

Can you identify the correct movie titles and deduce what principle is being applied?

▸ Charlie Harding's War

▸ King Cleveland

▸ The Eisenhower Show

▸ Get Reagan

▸ Jeremiah Nixon

26 OBSCENE TITLES

Can you identify the correct titles and work out the way in which they have been altered?

▸ Aegean's Eleven

▸ Electric Magnolias

▸ The True Tenenbaums

▸ Navy Grit

▸ Royal Kool-Aid Acid Test

▸ Baby in Wonderland

(27) STRIP SEARCH

Can you complete this story?

▸ First, I was a band of buccaneers on the high seas

▸ Then, I was angry

▸ Next, I was a rodent that is often considered a pest

▸ Finally, I was _____ _____

(28) MUSIC MIX

Can you identify each of the following original music tracks, before they were re-mixed?

▸ Also a Salt Bathtub – Rather Moaning

▸ Angered – Mourns Bar

▸ I Dislike Rags – Perky Tray

▸ Sack by Ex – Junk Albeit Merits

▸ A Vivid Lava – Dopy Call

▸ House of Pay – Hears Need

▸ Wail Lively As You Low – Why Shout In Tone

(29) GEM OF A PUZZLE

I'm needed for curling, and I am many a pound.
I can be a punishment, and I'm seen on the ground.
But get me in the kidneys, and pain will be found.
What am I?

(30) CAPITAL LETTERS

Where am I going?

▶ Low budget film   _ - _ _ _ _ _

▶ A sudden reversal in decision   _ - _ _ _ _

▶ 6th June 1944   _ - _ _ _

▶ Very famous person   _ - _ _ _ _ _ _

▶ Bent pipe under a sink   _ - _ _ _ _

▶ Region of ionosphere that reflects   _ - _ _ _ _ _ _
medium frequency radio waves

▶ Fast German railway line   _ - _ _ _ _

▶ Casually worn top   _ - _ _ _ _ _

Chapter 2

Computable

At a time when computers were in their infancy, Turing helped formalize the concept of a computable algorithm by inventing the Turing Machine, a simple, hypothetical machine which is capable of simulating any logical algorithm, no matter how complicated. Unlike other models of computation, Turing's was accessible and intuitive. Find out how creative and intuitive you can be too, with the more challenging puzzles in this second chapter.

① PIVOT POINTS

What unusual property do the following words all share?

- MAD
- ROT
- TEN
- DEW
- SAG
- LEV

② HOLY ORDERS

Place these confused entries into order:

- Burns me
- No remedy out
- Ex duos
- See sign
- Cut is vile

(3) MAN TO MAN

Can you join each pair of men by inserting two words so that each pair of adjacent words are synonyms? For example, you could join TAIL to COPY with TAIL > SHADOW > TRACE > COPY.

▶ ROB > _____ > _____ > JOSH

▶ PAT > _____ > _____ > MIDGE

▶ NICK > _____ > _____ > JOHN

▶ MARK > _____ > _____ > BILL

(4) A NEW TERM

Some children were sent to school – which one?
6 8 9 2 3 8 8 9 7 1 4 5 2 1 8 3 1 9

⑤ CAN YOU CONNECT

How can you connect the following words?

- ▶ Blood

- ▶ Dagger

- ▶ Curtains

- ▶ Bath

- ▶ Picture

- ▶ Audience

- ▶ Conclusion

⑥ ROUTE SUM

If you take away the common denominator in these events, but add their remaining parts, what sum would you obtain?

▸ Battle of Hastings

▸ Death of William the Bad of Sicily

▸ Battle of Benevento

▸ The Statutes of Kilkenny

▸ Death of Donatello

▸ Murder of David Rizzio in the Palace of Holyroodhouse

▸ Great Fire of London

▸ Britain's repeal of the Stamp Act

▸ Austro-Prussian War

▸ The Beatles' last live concert (that took place in San Francisco)

⑦ NAVIGRID

Place the digits 1 to 9 so that it is possible to jump from one digit to the next, in consecutive order, using the steps provided. Each step is an instruction to move a number of squares horizontally and/or vertically, and each must be used exactly once, in an order of your choosing. No part of a step can involve crossing over a black square.

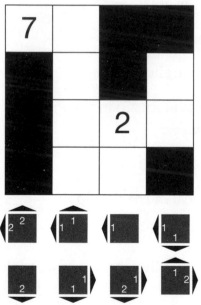

Can you complete each of these words so that they all repeat the same property?

- ＿ ＿ UR ＿ ＿
- ＿ ＿ SUL ＿ ＿
- ＿ ＿ ADAC ＿ ＿
- ＿ ＿ BL ＿ ＿
- ＿ ＿ CAP ＿ ＿
- ＿ ＿ G ＿ ＿
- ＿ ＿ HERN ＿ ＿
- ＿ ＿ CI ＿ ＿
- ＿ ＿ OTOGRA ＿ ＿
- ＿ ＿ CKLI ＿ ＿

(9) MISFORTUNE

The following items have a common feature to deduce:

▶ Millard Fillmore

▶ Lace

▶ I Chronicles

▶ Fra Mauro area, on the first attempt

▶ Abolition of slavery

▶ Ophiuchus

(10) ODD NAME OUT 2: VENGEANCE

Which of these fictional characters is the odd one out?

▶ Steve

▶ Natasha

▶ Clint

▶ Scott

▶ Tony

⑪ ELEPHANT DEVICES

The following mnemonics are used for remembering particular sequences. Can you identify them from their components? In some cases the sentence gives a hint to the nature of the sequence.

▸ Every Good Boy Deserves Fun

▸ My Very Eager Mother Just Served Us Nine Pizzas

▸ Bring Your Record Breaking Guy/Girl

▸ God's Eternal Love Never Dies

▸ Super Heroes Must Eat Oats

▸ Tall Girls Can Fight and Other Queer Things Can Develop

▸ Charmingly Nubile Ladies Mollify Debonair British Commander

(12) HIDDEN FLOWERS

Can you detect the five flowers hidden in the following passage?

Kew Gardens is a beloved place to stop off to see flowers from across the world. It always provides fantastic amusement to see the exotic names and variety of species. There have been many new ones placed into the collection, I learn. Even the most zealous enthusiast for flowers would have their interests satisfied. One can find useful information everywhere and some people concoct a gushing tribute at the end of their visit.

(13) PISCINE PHRASES

▶ The following statements contain 'fishy' elements. In some cases, the incidence occurs more than once. Can you find all thirteen?

▶ It's insupportable a king should abdicate when under pressure

▶ There's no desire in the general population for a long-forgotten church

▶ Toys termed intelligence elements are developed or yet to be used in other rings for spying operations

▶ Tourists escape lines in busy coastal port

▶ The lack of foreign languages in British education is a basic oddity

▶ People stop outside for drinkable treats

▶ All kinds of money emanate easily from a rich aristocrat

(14) FOUR BY FOUR I

Solve the clues and fit their answers into the 4×4 grid, so they read either across or down. Each answer is four letters long. To make things trickier, the clues are given in no particular order. One letter is already filled in.

- ▶ Now! (initials)
- ▶ Lids
- ▶ Counts at a gym
- ▶ Reduce difficulty
- ▶ Ensnare
- ▶ Badger's home
- ▶ A-lister, for example
- ▶ Tropical plant with edible root

			R

(15) TABLE OF COUNTRIES

Which country could follow next in this list?

- ▶ Colombia (6)
- ▶ Nicaragua (7)
- ▶ Oman (8)

(16) GLOBETROTTING I

Follow this journey, and answer the questions.

- ▶ I went to Casablanca, Vilnius and Vienna. Which island state did I visit after that?

- ▶ Then I went to Lisbon, Seville and Bujumbura. Which South American country was next on my itinerary?

- ▶ I saw Rome and visited Buenos Aires, then flew to Doha. Which Arab state did I go on to?

- ▶ And what did I say before setting off for Venice, Lagos, Bangkok, Nuku'alofa, Istanbul, Salzburg, Vatican City, Madrid, Luxembourg, Torshavn, Buenos Aires, Tblisi and Stockholm?

Shade some circles so that the remaining numbers are joined together into groups of one, two or three circles. The sum of the numbers in each group must match one of the totals provided. Each total is used exactly once. Groups may not touch each other, and neither may shaded circles.

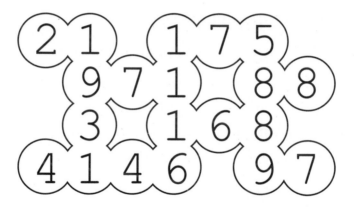

Totals: 5 6 7 9 12 22

⒙ VENN I

Can you identify the rule used to sort the elements in this Venn diagram?

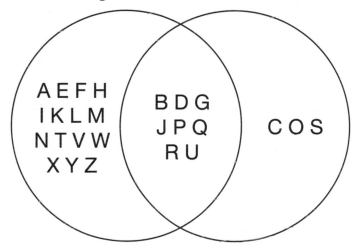

This wordsearch grid contains some hidden words, all at least four letters long, which can be written in any direction, either forwards or backwards, including diagonally. For the purposes of this puzzle, ignore any words of fewer than four letters. Once you have found the words, you will notice that every letter of the alphabet has been used at least once – except one. Which is that unused letter?

```
W Y B O P C F W I H
C U T A U I K Y A M
D Y E T Z B L E U M
E G D O E O U L O A
U M O S I R R I O I
E M S Q G E P J A W
U H N U P A T E X T
F N O I T C A R F I
I D V S P I F K L Y
F W K H S A N G B U
```

A B C D E F G H I J K L M N O P Q R S T U V W X Y Z

⑳ WHO'S NEXT?

The following names are arranged in a specific sequence. Enter an appropriate name in the empty last position.

▸ Bush

▸ Shakespeare

▸ Beckham

▸ Scissorhands

▸ Clooney

▸ Norton

▸ Harrison

▸ _____

(21) FEATURE

Can you identify the common feature of the following words?

- ▸ Castle

- ▸ Christmas

- ▸ Listen

- ▸ Often

- ▸ Hasten

- ▸ Rapport

- ▸ Gourmet

- ▸ Ballet

(22) WALL TO WALL

The answers to these clues zigzag back and forth across the grid, changing direction with each new line. The last letter of one answer is the first of the next. When you've finished, the shaded diagonal will spell out a mystery word.

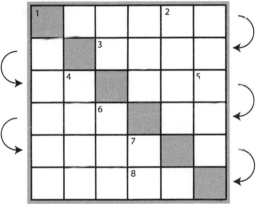

1. Continental quilt (5)
2. Garden songbird (6)
3. African canine carnivore (5)
4. Plant that gives liquorice its taste (5)
5. Land of Hope and Glory composer (5)
6. Sporting arbiter (7)
7. Stamp a design into paper (6)
8. Male deer (4)

(23) OBSCURE

I need water to form but I might give it back,

And I'm back up for you when your gadgets crack.

What am I?

(24) NEXT LINE

What comes next in the following lyrical sequence?

- ▸ 5GR

- ▸ 4CB

- ▸ 3FH

- ▸ 2TD

㉕ DOUBLE DUTY NAMES

The following nine capital cities can be divided into two groups of five. Which one is doing double duty?

- ▶ Athens

- ▶ Bamako

- ▶ Budapest

- ▶ Buenos Aires

- ▶ Copenhagen

- ▶ Islamabad

- ▶ Kigali

- ▶ Ottawa

- ▶ Sucre

(26) IT'S ALL AN ACT

Can you name the actor?

▸ Cuddly	_____	poodle
▸ Fairy	_____	teller
▸ Think	_____	apple
▸ Energy	_____	grace
▸ In	_____	investigator
▸ Meg	_____	Gosling
▸ Storm	_____	nine
▸ Road	_____	mountains

Use your word interrogation skills to decide what each of these six entries is hiding. Once fully revealed, two of them will be anagrams of one another.

▸ H

▸ H

▸ HA

▸ HE

▸ HER

▸ O

㉘ EVER-DECREASING CIRCLES

Visit every circle. What's the path?

START Years in a century	L	Single RPM	Steps	Strikes in three perfect games in bowling
Distance to the target in Olympic archery (m)	Squares on a checkered boardgame	The answer to Life, the Universe and Everything	Winks in a nap	FDR
Bryan Adams' Summer	Eleventh triangular number	Circles in this puzzle	Hendrix, Joplin and Winehouse's 'Club'	Days in four months?
First number with four 'E's	Noble gas group	Spots on a dice	Cats' Lives	Golf warning?
Sweet	3x3 magic square constant	Stripes on a US flag	German 'no'?	US international dial code

Chapter 3
Testing

In a 1950 paper Turing proposed
'The Imitation Game', a method of
judging whether a computer had become
'intelligent', which came to be known as the
Turing Test. The test simply states that if
a human tester cannot tell the difference
between the responses of a machine and the
responses of a human, then the machine
can be said to be intelligent. It's time now
to test your own intelligence, with this
chapter of tougher puzzles.

(I) BOARD

Six single words and one two-word term have a common property, and their outstanding feature could form something that is commonly associated with them. What is that thing?

▶ Crude

▶ Facet

▶ Tribe

▶ Amend

▶ Abound

▶ Snottily

▶ Poor niche

② FIVE BY FOUR

Can you group these words, names and phrases to form five non-overlapping sets? Each set will contain exactly four items.

CHESTNUT

RUSSET

BLINKY

HOOTER

FIZZY

DISCOVERY

FUJI

CLYDE

PINKY

BOILED

FAWN

JAZZ

CHEWY

MUG

NOODLE

CHOCOLATE

INKY

PINS

TAN

SOUR

③ THE MAN WITH THE GOLDEN PUN

Identify the following lesser-known motion pictures from these brief descriptions:

▸ You are given something solely for your female sheep

▸ Permission is given for an invoice to be sent

▸ The near future will bring only truth

▸ A scenic window looking over a small mountain

▸ Global warming must be stopped

▸ Perish in a future month

▸ Heirs to the throne who live it up in Las Vegas

▸ A hesitant refusal

▸ There is a limit to how many times you dance

(4) ESCAPED ANIMALS

Various animals have escaped from the sentences below. Can you restore them all? The number of letters in each animal's name is given after each sentence.

For example: 'Rat' has escaped from 'Came here to take photos' (3); once restored the sentence reads 'Camera there to take photos'.

▶ It's the dolly used to play with my friend (4)

▶ Which sis are stocked in the lingerie department? (5)

▶ Heard woman putting on clothes after bathing (5)

▶ Male beast to finish the race, having fallen first (5)

▶ Is a bully to rise from their bed in the spring? (4)

⑤ DIVERSITY TEST

The following items are in a particular sequence. A final element that continues the sequence is to be deduced.

▸ T H F R O by T C (3,6)

▸ A C O by A B (7,7)

▸ C Y by A H (6,6)

▸ A O G G by L M M (4,4,10)

▸ P B by T S (3,6)

▸ I by A H (5,7)

▸ _____

6 LIFE FORMS

Transform each word in the first column to make a new word in the second column, using the same transformation method for all rows. Next, transform each word in the second column to make a new word in the third column, again using the same transformation method for all rows (although this will be different from the method used to transform from column one to column two). Each word in the resulting third group will have something in common – what?

DOTE		
ROBE		
KILNS		
ASHORE		
DARE		
TEACHER		

⑦ NEXT IN LINE I

What should come next in each of the following real-world sequences, and why?

▸ M V E M J S

▸ F S T F F S

▸ I V X L C D

▸ M A M J J A

▸ F S S M T W

⑧ KEY WORDS

In what way might it be considered that the two words 'after-effects' and 'niminy-piminy' are opposite versions of the same phenomenon?

⑨ HOUSE-HUNTING

A series of common items in chronological order has to be deduced from the text. Each item is referred to by a definition and letter mixture in which the definition may precede or follow an anagram of the word's letters, and the set of letters for each anagram must start at the beginning of a word or finish at the end of a word. One member of the group (4-6-5) is missing and has to be deduced. Some sentences contain more than one item and the definition and letter mixture can appear across multiple sentences.

Wisdom, perhaps, in Roman natives or those given an area of western France is observed. Some get plate annually for Latin sprig of broom? Clear standards are seen from bomber during itinerary – OK. Bowl in stadium tour demonstrates a fine architectural style. Little, perhaps, found in a trust putting fruit on great display. Hear novel German city has left Barbara, maybe, struggling to react in words.

⑩ WORD ASSOCIATION

Complete the missing word from the final item:

▶ 11 = people (F)

▶ 14 = savage (F)

▶ 18 = worshipping figure (O)

▶ 27 = stupid (D)

▶ 29 = keeping guard (W)

▶ 38 = rope (C)

▶ 39 = haggle (B)

▶ 41 and 43 = stream (G)

▶ 45 = _____ (F)

(11) THEMED PAIRS

Form four common pairs from the following group of items:

► De-creasing

► Firedog

► Flower with yellow or orange heads

► Glittering paper

► Implore

► 18th century Irish dramatist

► Swift-flying songbird

► Starring

(12) MUSICAL WORDS

Each of these phrases suggests a seven-letter word, with those words arranged in alphabetical order. Can you identify the musical feature they have in common?

▸ Came to the throne

▸ Emotional problems

▸ Round vegetable

▸ Spoiled by overwriting

▸ Removed to render invisible

▸ Main front of a building

▸ Choked

A BIT TO EAT

Six teenagers went for a meal at the A1 Cafe. They soon realized, however, that one item was missing from the menu. Can you figure out what it was, too?

Here's what they ate:

	Apple pie	Ice cream	Burger	Fries	Drink
Anne		✓			
Barney		✓	✓	✓	✓
Coleen	✓		✓		
David			✓		
Erica		✓	✓	✓	✓
Frank			✓	✓	✓

Can you identify the rules used to sort the elements in this Venn diagram?

AUTHORITATIVE COMMENTS

Can you identify the common source of comments contained in the following pieces of text, all of which have been treated in the same way?

- RDMY LPSN NWT XS

- THNL YTHN GWHV TFRS FRTS LF

- MYFL LWMRC NSSK NTWH TYRC NTRYC NDFR YSKW HTYC NDFRY RCNTRY

- NVRT RSTM NNLS SVGT HSPC KRNM YPCKT

- FYWN TFRN DNW SHNG TNG TDG

- BLSS DRTH YNGFR THYSHL LNHRT THNT NLDBT

- YMYF LLLT HPPL SMF THTM YCNV NFLS MFTH PPLL LTHT MBT YCN TFL LLFT HPPL LLTHTM

⒃ CLIMBER'S DIVISION

Can you identify eight members of a noted group suggested by the following hints (both cryptic and straight), finding the missing member?

▸ UK prime minister

▸ South American country broadcast

▸ Former US grunge musician

▸ British naval college

▸ Dutch territory?

▸ Singer with weight

▸ Key supplier

⒄ PERIODIC PAIRS

Can you split the following items into pairs by applying them to different members of a noted group? Some items could suit several members, were it not necessary to form them into pairs.

Ash	Black
Bloody	Casual
Cyber	Good
Holy	Lazarus
Maundy	Palm
Plough	Shrove
Spy	Super

⒅ BILINGUAL GIBBERISH

The following phrases express the same sentiment in four different languages. Can you identify the key phrase, hinted at by the title, that would be used in English?

▶ Parang intsik

▶ Questo per me è arabo

▶ Gi estas Volapuko por mi

▶ C'est du chinois

BACK TO THE BEGINNING?

The following is a table of contents illustrating a set of items. Can you identify the other letter that has to accompany E as corresponding to 10?

- ▶ 4: B × 2 , F, P, T

- ▶ 5: A × 2 , G, H, N, O, T × 2

- ▶ 6: A, C, H, M, P, R, T × 2, W

- ▶ 7: C, H, J × 3, K, L, M

- ▶ 8: B, C, F, G, H × 2, M, V

- ▶ 9: C, J, R × 2

- ▶ 10: E, _____

⑳ LEADERS OF THE GODS

The numbers below represent translations of the names of the Olympian gods. Can you complete the missing number?

- ▶ Zeus = -16
- ▶ Hera = +2
- ▶ Poseidon = -2
- ▶ Demeter = -1
- ▶ Athena = +12
- ▶ Apollo = +0
- ▶ Artemis = +3
- ▶ Ares = +12
- ▶ Aphrodite = +21
- ▶ Hephaestus = +14
- ▶ Hermes = +5
- ▶ Hestia = +14
- ▶ Dionysus = _____ _____ __

(21) PUNAGRAMS 3

Solve the anagrams below to reveal eight sports. However, each anagram has one letter missing. In order, these missing letters read to give an answer to this question:

What sport do Phoebe, Monica, Rachel, Chandler and Joey play? (4,4)

- ► FOG   _____   _

- ► CHERRY   _____   _

- ► SCORE   _____   _

- ► TALL BABES   _____   _

- ► OK NOSE   _____   _

- ► SUM   _____   _

- ► NEWT GIRL   _____   _

- ► QUASH   _____   _

(22) MISSION ACTIVITY

Each word in the following list has a common property to be found. The leftovers can then be arranged to denote something that might be used to describe their activity.

▶ Pliant

▶ Krona

▶ Lemon

▶ Negate

▶ Peerless

▶ Putto

▶ Reforming

▶ Sedate

▶ Unbelt

(23) NUMBER SEQUENCE

What number and city would be next in the following sequence?

▸ 2 = Sydney

▸ 6 = Athens

▸ 10 = Beijing

▸ 5 = London

(24) TABLE OF CITIES

Which city could follow next in this list?

▸ Galway (31)

▸ Geneva (32)

▸ Asmara (33)

▸ Seattle (34)

(25) LANGUAGE TOUR

Can you identify which places would be being referred to in the following list, if you were in each given country at the time?

▶ Mailand (Germany)

▶ Monaco (Italy)

▶ Aix-la-Chapelle (France)

▶ Rijsel (Holland)

▶ Wien (Germany)

▶ Bryste (Wales)

▶ Ginebra (Spain)

▶ Pressburg (Germany)

(26) ALAN'S CURIOUS QUEST

Follow the clues chronologically to locate a Narnian treasure on the map below.

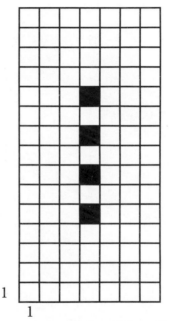

▶ Lucy Looks into a Wardrobe / How Shasta Set Out on His Travels / The Island / The Picture in the Bedroom / Behind the Gym/ Jill is Given a Task / The Sailing of the King

- Back on This Side of the Door / Prince Corin / The Storm and What Came of It / Puddleglum/

- A Day with the Beavers / Aravis in Tashbaan / How the Adventure Ended/ The Hill of the Strange Trenches / The House of Harfang / How They Discovered Something Worth Knowing / The Island of the Voices / Across the Desert / In the Witch's House / What Happened After Dinner

- In the Dark Castle / The Dufflepuds Made Happy / The Unwelcome Fellow Traveller / Aslan is Nearer / Peter's First Battle / Deep Magic from the Dawn of Time / The Fight at Anvard / The High King in Command / The Three Sleepers / Underland Without the Queen

- The Disappearance of Jill

(27) **MIDDLESIX**

Arrange the letters of the word CAFETERIA into the empty grid squares to create six five-letter words, three reading across and three reading down.

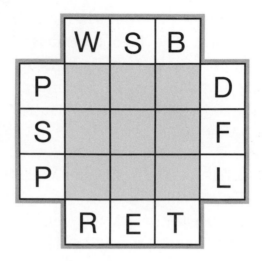

Chapter 4

Encrypted

Turing made many breakthroughs during
his work on codebreaking at Bletchley Park
in the 1940s. Some of his methods were so
important that they were only declassified
as recently as 2012, remaining useful and
relevant for 70 years — a remarkable amount
of time, when you consider the advances
in computing that have taken place since
then. See if you too can crack some thornier
problems in this next chapter — which
includes some encrypted text.

① BLETCHLEY PARK CROSSWORD

Bletchley Park once used a cryptic crossword to find recruits for its early code-cracking efforts. Try solving *this* themed cryptic puzzle, noting that perimeter letters are significant.

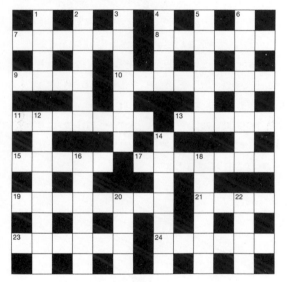

ACROSS

7. Making inquiry in a ruling capacity? (6)
8. Personal declaration by ex-PM, we hear, forming part for viewer (3-3)

9. Very little military intelligence on province (4)
10. Learner suffering to lose strength (8)
11. Computers etc staged for analysis following essence of logic (7)
13. Hotel by a top Asian capital (5)
15. Decorators – leaderless people taking risks? (5)
17. Allows modern technology in waves (7)
19. Inactive before start of decryption regarding some codes? (8)
21. University lecturer first with note in game (4)
23. Those ending intelligence mission connect order (6)
24. Side with number of characters in cryptograph? (6)

DOWN
1. It could be found among Verona's tipple? (4)
2. Income not recorded mostly in government (6)
3. Serviceman fired among outsiders in agency showing suppleness (7)
4. Element found in machine once (4)
5. Jellyfish in sea by home of the CIA (6)
6. Capital court's assembled for youth following planes, maybe (3, 5)
12. Advantage in a manning of operations, it's said (8)
14. Stop in back making one more prepared (7)
16. Fine material in bands for part of typewriter (6)
18. Spymaster given independent place as surroundings (6)
20. Foreign queen in country after leader's demoted (4)
22. Limited intake that is filling decoding team originally (4)

② FLAG TIME

What type of flag do the following times represent?

► 10:00

► 3:45

► 7:50

► 6:45

► 6:35

► 4:40

► 6:00

(3) FIRST REVISIONS

Can you work out what I was doing at 11pm?

- ▸ At 2am, I was conveying

- ▸ At 6am, I was worrying

- ▸ At 7am, I was putting on a harness

- ▸ At 8am, I was listening

- ▸ At 2pm, I was approaching

- ▸ At 6pm I was raising

- ▸ At 7pm, I was cauterizing

- ▸ At 8pm, I was ripping

- ▸ At 11pm, I was ___ _____

④ THE LONG AND SHORT OF IT

What am I doing here?

Taking each word,

And hearing

How it sounds.

One for dit. Two

For dah.

Keeping fit

Running. Handsome Morse?

⑤ FOUR BY FOUR 2

Solve the clues and fit their answers into the 4×4 grid, so they read either across or down. Each answer is four letters long. To make things trickier, the clues are given in no particular order. One letter is already filled in.

▸ Keep out of sight

▸ Routes

▸ Eastern European capital

▸ Food

▸ Leer

▸ Social insects

▸ In a carefree manner

▸ Child's bed

(6) NO MAN'S LAND

I have some strange codes in my passport. Where have I been?

- ▸ FVGLZ KPWQS NYJRT ADBUH

- ▸ GWTPF LJVEX KYIQB MZC

- ▸ JSOQP TIYUZ GXWFH BLVC

- ▸ LJWDY CRPGQ HXVOF M

- ▸ YGOPM JFUXH QVCKB

- ▸ IDOFS WKBLZ XECMQ JPTV

- ▸ WMSOD IQVXJ TBUYL GKPZH

- ▸ HRWPZ XQKJF BUDYT MGC

- ▸ CUGQF JKWPR HZSDY XLOB

- ▸ JFVXN CQZIK YGOPT DWHM

⑦ MORTPANTEAUX

How should these words be more properly spelled?

▶ PARIONETTE: _ _ _ _ _ _ _

▶ ROLETUME: _ _ _ _ _ _ _

▶ HOMBAY: _ _ _ _ _ _ _ _ _

▶ FOON: _ _ _ _ _

▶ POMERINE: _ _ _ _ _ _ _ _

▶ LEAKFAST: _ _ _ _ _ _ _ _

▶ FOKE: _ _ _ _ _

▶ CAMFORD: _ _ _ _ _ _ _ _

▶ EGANTIC: _ _ _ _ _ _ _ _ _

▶ RIDEO: _ _ _ _

⑧ STEP-BY-STEP

If you solve this puzzle in a step-by-step way, you will end up with one, appropriate, word. What is that word?

▸ 4922945 1452420 12914519 225 2081855

▸ 55567554585 4357260 38743557

▸ 124506 33936 1625763 727623 243574539

▸ 117405844867569634353961173 755202633 155442

⑨ NEXT IN LINE 2

What should come next in each of the following real-world sequences, and why?

▶   O   T   T   F   F   S

▶   V   I   B   G   Y   O

▶   M   N   B   V   C   X

▶   H   H   L   B   B   C

▶   C   G   D   A   E   B

Thanks to recent developments, such occurrences are now fortunately rather rare – but under what circumstances might a barmaid be seen to create carnage, with Smirnoff being poisoned and a pint likely to get you shot?

(11) MIXING PAINT

The three 'rails' on a fence need painting, but which three paints should be used?

P L A T W U P E C R E B O N R S L R

(12) WAVE DOWN

Here's the ripest mix-up. For each line, flag up what is happening and calculate the missing answer. If you get cross, that may be a sign.

▶ Netherlands, Scotland, Ukraine   = 6

▶ Thailand, Switzerland, Russia   = 8

▶ USA, Jamaica, Japan   = 0

▶ Germany, England, Argentina   = _____

Solve the clues, which are arranged alphabetically in order of their full solution. Enter them where they fit, so as to fill the crossword grid. Bars indicate the ends of entries.

Is there a problem? (4)
Disagree (2)
Bohemian (2)
Intense watch (3)
Netanyahu (2)
Sweetheart (2)
Secretive (2)
Tropical resin (3)
Cockney greeting (2)
Void (2)
Power (3)
Jealousy (2)
Here in France (2)
You've done me a favour (3)
Understand (2)
Spanish relative (2)
Monkey (2)
Palish (2)

TWO BOYS

Five members of a historical group are to be identified in the table below. Reading across the table, each relates in the same way to the different members of the group.

ECHO GROUP	BREAKDOWN GROUP	TYPE GROUP
Tree pitch	As a hotel	Montana
Northern Ireland town sea fog	Award a hectare	Lincoln
Converted a try	Proceed lord	Palladium
Alaskan capital	Month zero	Diana
Flock of mallards	Special language unit	Spear

15 WORD SQUARE

The answers to each of the three parts of this question consist of three letters. When you have solved each part, write the answers in order from top to bottom in the 3×3 grid. The name of a person is then traceable in the grid, although letters may be visited more than once.

▶ What three-letter acronym can be inserted into all of the following words to make four new words?
Coder, pet, seat, sting

▶ What real word could be consistent in meaning with the following unreal words?
Etalp, latem, nac, yenom

▶ Which set of letters starts words with the following meanings in ascending order of size?
Food, rough, US rock music, complaint

(16) **OPERATIONS**

Solve the cryptic clues below and write the answers in the grid, which will then give you a thirteenth one in the central column. The clues also provide openings to an additional hint as to the identity of the thirteenth item, barring an indefinite article.

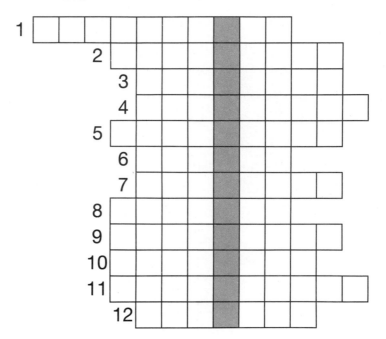

1. Bungling aim with confused males surrounding church festival (10)

2. Rockfall in this area, northern Switzerland, in a depressed feature (9)

3. In charge of peer and superior (8)

4. Device in winery, perhaps, with Irish port's staff (9)

5. Grub nice team cooked after mass (9)

6. Especially prickly plant caught in California by American (6)

7. Troubling changes, not for all to see in fastener (8)

8. Ox-like creature in New York city (7)

9. One that could be called upon for engagement? (9)

10. Fall behind rate unusually – an emotional sign (8)

11. Awkwardly move sailor, worker in timber (10)

12. Rollicking grandee making explosive device (7)

(17) STACKED TIPS

Can you identify the common property of the words with the given meanings in the following stack? The words are of increasing length in the stack, and the clue to each word is a definition of the full word plus a cryptic indication of the remainder of the word that *excludes* the common property.

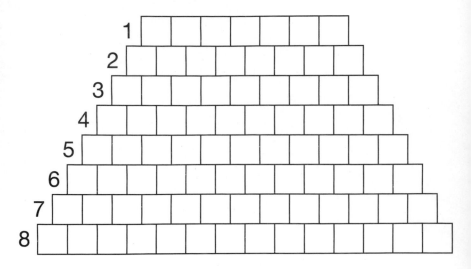

1. Expert soprano

2. Irrational number breathes

3. One badgering servants?

4. Style of music by Frenchman in a luring process?

5. Return of horrible figure around river in secret

6. Gas or liquid containing iodine in description of natural phenomena

7. Diversion in a term that's altered

8. Sprayer, say, one for each gentleman containing phosphorus

⒙ TRANSFORMATIONS

Match up the five final clues to their other halves.

PALE	♣	Bucket
	♦	Jump *or* Bell sound
	♥	Friend
	♠	Force 8 wind *or* Story

DAMP   ♥ ♠ ♦ ♠ ♣ _____

EARTH   ♦ ♥ ♠ ♦ ♥ _____

STUDY   ♦ ♥ ♠ ♥ ♦ _____

STAGE   ♦ ♥ ♣ ♠ ♣ _____

YEARLY   ♠ ♥ ♥ ♣ ♠ _____

▸ Hawaiian garment

▸ Head covering

▸ Heaviness

▸ Sandwich

▸ Scrap of cloth

(19) VENN 3

Can you identify the rule used to sort the elements in this Venn diagram?

Untangle each triplet of related words. The letters in each puzzle are in the correct order for each component word, but the components can be mixed in any way.

For example, SILGOBVLERRONZED = GOLD, SILVER and BRONZE

- PROLONGSPLIVERE

- THRONETWEEO

- LOBSTARRECLOCKK

- HARDTRICKYOM

- WARWILDROTICOBHEN

- CARDPAROVERMINAROGOATTSI

- APARTOARHOTMISSHOS

- SCRAPNOCKPLEAP

- BRAMAROURBRINICEY

Chapter 5

Enigmatic

Cracking the enciphered text produced by the Enigma machine was the ultimate test for Alan Turing and his colleagues at Bletchley Park. Now it's time for your own ultimate test — can you crack the hardest puzzles this book has to offer?

① ODD PAIR OUT I

The following twelve words can be joined into six pairs. Which is the odd pair out?

- ▶ Adult

- ▶ Antic

- ▶ Bouts

- ▶ Clone

- ▶ Deter

- ▶ Lines

- ▶ Orate

- ▶ Paste

- ▶ Rated

- ▶ Riser

- ▶ There

- ▶ Tramp

② GRIDFILL I

Fill the grid below with letters, one to each square, in such a way that each one of the seven shades of the rainbow – RED, ORANGE, YELLOW, GREEN, BLUE, INDIGO and VIOLET – can be traced by starting at a letter and moving through adjacent squares horizontally and vertically, but not diagonally. Double letters must occupy two adjacent squares.

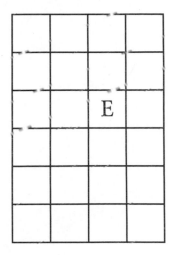

Extract one letter from each of the following words, in a logical and consistent way, to form a seven-letter word. Using the same logic, which letter can then be extracted from this word?

► PILFER

► BLABBER

► NOMINATE

► ENQUIRED

► CLATTER

► TRIFLE

► BASTE

④ WORD MAESTRO

Can you identify the common language link in the following?

▸ Drowsiness from eating a big meal

▸ Lady who looks after stray cats

▸ To rest in the shade on a hot day

▸ A really badly made drink

⑤ POP SUMS I

If Smalltown Boy = More Than In Love, then solve (ignoring definite articles):

▸ One Week = Make It With You + _____

▸ Viva La Vida + Big Log + The First Picture Of You
  = Pure Morning + Refugees + _____ + _____

⑥ OLD AND NEW

Can you join the following terms into pairs that fit together to make the clues to a particular set of words?

- ► Actual

- ► Aural

- ► Axe

- ► Broadsheet

- ► Cooker

- ► Cut

- ► Dawdler

- ► Match

- ► Morning

- ▶ Movie
- ▶ Post
- ▶ Presumptuous
- ▶ Racket sport
- ▶ Reserve
- ▶ Speechless
- ▶ Standard
- ▶ Transmit
- ▶ Unbending

(7) HUNT THE CHARACTER

Three components of a descriptive phrase are to be deduced in various ways. The phrase then has to be jumbled to form the name of a character.

The first component (2,8) has three different hints:

▸ The first is a standard cryptic clue: Supply free moralist as a prototype (8,4)

▸ The second can be defined as 'article' (2) followed by 'peculiarity' (6), creating a two-word term (2,6)

▸ The third could be depicted as: pe or imittion (3,1,4) – the method of describing either could be seen as a loose and somewhat whimsical definition of the component

The second component (5), which as a hint would be given as (4) in US English, has three exemplary cryptic clues each without a definition. Their common field forms the component. These are:

▸ Drink covering good cups? (8)

- Record freeze falling short (5)

- Hardened skin around much of incision (8)

The third component (3) has triple associations:

- The first is a word property demonstrated in a mixed-up, additive sense by the following: demon, taupe and notion

- The second is a word property that the following three words have in common: case, hatch, shell

- The third consists of synonyms that could be defined as polish (4) and cool (3)

The resulting phrase can be sifted to form a key character (4,8,6).

⑧ VENN 4

Can you identify the rule used to sort the elements in this Venn diagram?

France, India, China, Norway, Russia

Gabon, Ecuador, Brazil, Indonesia, Kenya

Argentina, New Zealand, Papua New Guinea, Samoa, South Africa

⑨ ISOLATE

Draw walls to partition the grid into six areas, such that each area contains two stars. The six areas must each have one of the sizes shown beneath the grid, in terms of the number of squares that make up that area. Each '+' must be linked to at least two walls, and each listed area size must be used exactly once.

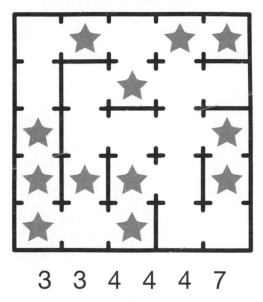

3   3   4   4   4   7

(10) CRYPTIC MOVIE CLUB

The schedule for our Movie Club this season has been devised by a crossword setter, who has imagined each movie title to be a cryptic clue with a one-word solution. For example, OBSESS = Horrible Bosses (anagram of BOSSES), CHILL = Cold Mountain (C+HILL), and POM = Love In The Afternoon (O in PM). From the following list of 'solutions', can you identify the original titles? The length of each word in the original movie title is given.

- ► AM (3,5,7)

- ► SCREWABLE (3,2,5)

- ► TAN (4,1,8)

- ► VINOUS (3,5,5)

- ► KEITH (4,4,2,3)

- ► EVOLVE (3,5,3)

- ► BIG (1,4,4,8)

(11) TITLE FEATURES

What common feature do the following movie titles all share? The years are provided as additional clues.

▸ Life of Brian (1968)

▸ Theatre of Blood (1995)

▸ The Krays (2004)

▸ A Clockwork Orange (1985)

▸ Brazil (1969)

▸ Babel (1995)

▸ Fargo (2012)

⑫ GRIDFILL 2

Fill the grid below with letters, one to each square, in such a way that each one of the seven deadly sins – AVARICE, ENVY, GLUTTONY, LUST, PRIDE, SLOTH and WRATH – can be traced by starting at a letter and moving through adjacent squares horizontally and vertically, but not diagonally. What's more, the letters occupying the first and third rows spell two words that have the same meaning, although the first is archaic usage. What are those words? Double letters must occupy two adjacent squares, and squares can be revisited within a word.

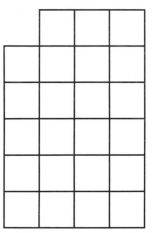

⒀ GLOBETROTTING 2

Which word is the 'longest'?

- ▸ MADDEN

- ▸ SEAMAN

- ▸ BOMBOS

- ▸ LAXIST

- ▸ HELLAS

(14) EVEN MORE TANGLED TRIOS

Untangle each triplet of related words. The letters in each puzzle are in the correct order for each component word, but the components can be mixed in any way.

For example, SILGOBVLERRONZED = GOLD, SILVER and BRONZE

- ► CLAMOURRELYRY

- ► SHAMTIMERRRANUVIPL

- ► BLEATTCOMATOUTCONE

- ► LSMEARMADIGULLME

- ► FEARWITHINRED

- ► SHINLIKEROOKNE

- ► BAGDOUGLODY

- ► PALTUTORAMAINEOBINSLESS

- ► SLOGAILSQUIDID

(15) VENN 5

Can you identify the rule used to sort the elements in this Venn diagram?

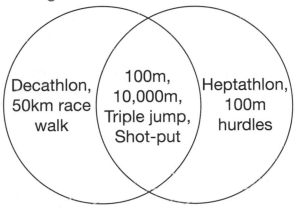

(16) APT PROPERTY

In what way do the letters in the word EQUATION form an equation?

(17) DIGITALLY ENHANCED JIGSAW

Solve the clues, which are arranged alphabetically in order of their full solution. Enter them where they fit, so as to fill the crossword grid. Bars indicate the ends of entries.

Whichever (2)

Earlier (2)

Not harmful (2)

Dog (2)

Stray (3)

What's seized in Latin (2)

Waste away (4)

Arise (3)

Pictogram (3)

Scientific crime department (3)

Horse (2)

Shortest lines between points (4)

S-shaped moulding (2)

An essential amino acid (3)

French river and department (2)

(18) ODD PAIR OUT 2

The following twelve words can be divided into six pairs.
Which is the odd pair out?

▸ Absent

▸ Boar

▸ Bucks

▸ Darkness

▸ Demand

▸ Distant

▸ Heavy

▸ Open

▸ Reap

▸ Receive

▸ Rigidly

▸ Undoes

⑲ POP SUMS 2

If Elvis Presley + Coldplay + Radiohead + Prince = Right Said Fred, then complete the following equations:

▶ Spice Girls + Olivia Newton-John + Adele + Kenny Ball & His Jazzmen = _____

▶ _____ + Spandau Ballet + Commodores + Sweet = _____

⑳ ALPHABETIC EXTRACTION

There are three different keys on a key ring: a car key, a house key and a factory key. Unfortunately, the owner has forgotten which key unlocks each item, but luckily there is some writing on each key, as shown below. Can you work out which key, when correctly inserted, unlocks each item?

▶ Key 1: V K N G P B K L

▶ Key 2: C U T N L N A H K D

▶ Key 3: P E Q D S E K U E

(21) GRIDFILL 3

Fill the grid below with letters, one to each square, in such a way that each one of the seven sages of Greece – BIAS, CHILON, CLEOBULUS, PERIANDER, PITTACUS, SOLON and THALES – can be traced by starting at a letter and moving through adjacent squares horizontally and vertically, but not diagonally. Double letters must occupy two adjacent squares, and squares can be revisited within a word. To help you, two identical configurations of four letters have been marked with shaded squares.

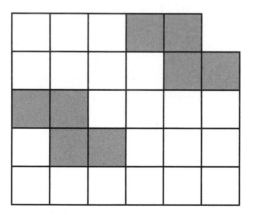

(22) FIND THE ACTRESS

Solve the clues and find the actress:

- ▸ Angled

- ▸ Baby's shoe

- ▸ Body louse

- ▸ Curbed

- ▸ Mountainside basin (Scot)

- ▸ Punched

- ▸ Scrounged (Aust)

- ▸ Soccer

- ▸ Started up (a computer)

- ▸ To potter

- ▸ To snuggle (Scot)

- ▸ Town near Liverpool

- ▸ Was of the correct size

Recognized as a HDQCMOCI HAPSTJ of AJPOHONOAG OCPTGGOITCNT with creations such as the AQPDBAPON NDBEQPOCI TCIOCT among his works, this pioneer created the PQJOCI BANSOCT which became a landmark in its field.

His final research was entitled PST NSTBONAG LAKOK DH BDJESDITCTKOK (published in 1952) describing the way in which non-uniformity may arise naturally out of a homogeneous, uniform state.

Can you deduce the cipher code to determine the name of the person for whom this tribute is given?

Hints

Every puzzle has at least one hint, but most puzzles have several. They are intended to be read one-by-one in order, so when you are stuck on a puzzle, read just the first hint and see if it helps. If you remain stuck, then return and read the second hint, and then so on and so on for the remainder of the hints until you — hopefully — make progress on the puzzle.

HINTS FOR CHAPTER I:
DECIPHERABLE

(I) FLOWER POWER

▶ Flower Power/flowery language means there is something to do with flowers in each sentence

▶ Each sentence contains the name of a flower hidden within the text

(2) MOVIE EDITS

▶ These are strange phrases – what could be going on?

▶ They are anagrams of movie titles

(3) WORD CONNECTIONS

▶ The first column is FIRE ARM BAND, creating the terms FIREARM and ARMBAND

▶ The missing word on the right is MAN

(4) END OF SERIES

▶ Everything you need to know is on the page

▶ Take a look at the words asking the question

▶ Consider the final letters

(5) WHAT THE...?

▶ The title is a clue – what comes next in that phrase?
▶ What is missing from the characters listed?
▶ There are no vowels – you must restore them
▶ They are Dickens characters

(6) CLOCK SCHEDULING

▶ This requires historical knowledge, which you could look up online or in a reference book
▶ Each line refers to a battle
▶ Each time refers to a year

(7) COMPLETE THE PICTURE

▶ The same letters are missing from each line
▶ The title is a clue

(8) PUNAGRAMS I

▶ The first letter to remove is S
▶ The first country is famous for chocolate and Hercule Poirot
▶ The second letter to remove is P
▶ The third letter to remove is R
▶ The fourth letter to remove is A

(9) TETRA-DROP GRID FILL

▶ Piece 1 could fit in one of four positions, but it can't go on the far left or else piece 2 couldn't fit

- ▶ Once you place piece 1, piece 2 must fit onto piece 1, either off the left or on top of it, otherwise there'd be a gap below
- ▶ You need to spell words too, so experiment with how piece 3 can fit
- ▶ Once you have the first few pieces placed, the rest is straightforward
- ▶ Piece 1 goes at the bottom right
- ▶ Piece 2 goes in columns 3 and 4
- ▶ Piece 3 goes in columns 1 and 2

(10) QUOTE HANJIE

- ▶ This puzzle can be solved with pure logic – no guessing needed. The key thing to do is to mark squares that are definitely part of the quote, as well as squares that are definitely shaded
- ▶ You can cross-reference deductions back and forth between rows and columns until the puzzle is solved
- ▶ Row 1, when shaded, leaves THOSE
- ▶ Row 2, when shaded, leaves WHOCAN
- ▶ The final row, when shaded, leaves IBLE

(11) ANAGRAM CONNECTIONS I

- ▶ The first anagram solution starts with CO____
- ▶ The fifth anagram starts with PL_____
- ▶ The final anagram starts with MA____
- ▶ What word can go before or after each solved anagram?

(12) PUNAGRAMS 2

▶ The first anagram starts with C
▶ The first anagram starts CO___
▶ The second anagram starts A
▶ The second anagram starts AR___

(13) COMMON FEATURES I

▶ They are strange phrases – why?
▶ They are anagrams
▶ They are anagrams of the same kind of thing
▶ The last one ends with 'ton'

(14) ODD NAME OUT I

▶ Why does it mention Oscar?
▶ Are these just names, or is there another connection too?
▶ It refers to the Oscars – the movie awards
▶ They are all names of movies

(15) THE VAULT

▶ There is an 'X' on the left. There aren't many words of the form 'EX__'
▶ There also aren't many that read 'EW__'
▶ Can you find a rotation of the dials that makes words for both of these?

WHERE AM I?

- ▶ How many times is 'SE' repeated in the first one?
- ▶ Try saying the count and 'SE' out loud
- ▶ They are rebuses – words represented by combinations of sounds from letters and pictures
- ▶ The first one is ten SE
- ▶ The first one is Tennessee
- ▶ The second has 'ILL' inside 'OIS'
- ▶ The third is a picture of a road followed by what?
- ▶ The fourth is an 'M' on some letters
- ▶ The fifth is an anagram
- ▶ For the fifth, a way of cluing an anagram is to say 'new'
- ▶ The penultimate one is written right-to-left

17 **COMMON FEATURES 2**

- ▶ The 'reference' referred to is a dictionary
- ▶ What do you spot in common between the definitions?
- ▶ What can you 'derive' – what derivations are in a dictionary?
- ▶ Where do the words come from?

18 **WATCH THIS**

- ▶ Why is it called 'Watch This'?
- ▶ It refers to movie titles
- ▶ What is missing from the titles?

19 ALTERNATIVE EXPRESSIONS

▶ What does the first entry remind you of?

▶ Think of the title

▶ Think of common expressions

20 ANAGRAM CONNECTIONS 2

▶ You're looking for a word that can go either before or after all of the solved anagrams

21 SIX MIX

▶ The first line is an anagram of KINDLE

▶ And the second is an anagram of STREAM

▶ The other anagrams are IMPURE, CURATE, PORTAL and CAMPED

22 KEY NUMBERS

▶ What is a 'key number'?

▶ Or, more particularly, what is a 'number key'?

▶ It's on a keyboard

▶ What else is on the number?

23 CONNECTION

▶ What country does 'cafetière' hail from?

▶ What is an alternative name for a cafetière?

▶ Can you think of a type of salad accompaniment?

▶ And what is eggy bread called?

- ▶ Another word for fried potatoes is... what?
- ▶ What is the common term?

㉔ LITERARY SET

- ▶ How is it a 'literary set'?
- ▶ The connection is books
- ▶ Each book has been modified in some way
- ▶ Can you guess at any of the original titles? What has changed?
- ▶ The first title should be The Crow Road
- ▶ How does Murder connect to Crow?
- ▶ The second title should be H is for Hawk

㉕ MOVIE CLUB

- ▶ Do these look a bit like real movie titles?
- ▶ What has changed in each case?
- ▶ The first one should be Charlie Wilson's War
- ▶ What connects Wilson to Harding?
- ▶ The second should be King Arthur

㉖ OBSCENE TITLES

- ▶ What can you spot in common between all the titles?
- ▶ Why is the puzzle called 'obscene titles'?
- ▶ Do the titles remind you of real movie or book titles?
- ▶ The first should be Ocean's Eleven
- ▶ What is another term for an obscene movie?

(27) STRIP SEARCH

▶ Why is it called 'strip search'?

▶ At each step the answer is 'stripped'

▶ The band of buccaneers are pirates

▶ You now know all you need to know! Read the above again!

(28) MUSIC MIX

▶ 'Re-mixed' indicates anagrams – they are anagrams of song titles and their artists

▶ The first one is by an artist with initials M T

▶ The first one is by Meghan Trainor

▶ The last one is by an artist with initials W H

▶ The last one is by Whitney Houston

(29) GEM OF A PUZZLE

▶ What is a 'gem'?

▶ What type of thing is it?

▶ What is made up of pounds?

(30) CAPITAL LETTERS

▶ What do the _ - _ _ _ _ etc entries on the right mean?

▶ What is the hyphen for?

▶ You are looking for hyphenated words

- The number of letters is shown
- Look for solutions to the clues. The first is B-movie
- What is the title again?
- Look at all the initial letters

HINTS FOR CHAPTER 2:
COMPUTABLE

(I) PIVOT POINTS

▶ Most of the words, but not all, can also be read backwards

▶ This isn't the answer, but it's quite close – what does 'Pivot points' refer to?

▶ What if you 'pivot' the word on its final letter?

(2) HOLY ORDERS

▶ 'Confused' indicates anagrams

▶ What is the 'holy' order?

(3) MAN TO MAN

▶ ROB changes first of all to MUG

▶ And if you are mugging, you are...

▶ ...fooling around – so MUG changes to FOOL

▶ To fool around is to josh about, so the first one is finished.

▶ The second puzzle changes first of all to an anagram of the given word

▶ The third puzzle goes first to a four-letter word that starts with a J

▶ The fourth puzzle goes first to a four-letter word starting with S

(4) A NEW TERM

▶ Try writing the numbers out in words

▶ What do you spot, initially?

(5) CAN YOU CONNECT

▶ You can do something to all of them

▶ You can ___ a curtain, for example

(6) ROUTE SUM

▶ The Battle of Hastings took place in which year?

▶ Look up the other events. What years did they take place?

▶ So what is in common, and what is the sequence?

(7) NAVIGRID

▶ The '1 left and 1 down' must be used to escape from the top square in the rightmost column, if it's not the 9

▶ There are only two possible moves from the 7 – right 1 and down 1, and right 1 and down 2

▶ For each of those possible moves, what would come next?

▶ Experiment with possible routes, making pencil-mark notes of your deductions

(8) SO IT BEGINS (AND ENDS)

▶ The title tells you pretty much what to do
▶ The first solution is CHURCH
▶ The second is INSULIN
▶ Can you spot the connection?

(9) MISFORTUNE

▶ Who was Millard Fillmore?
▶ What does lace celebrate?
▶ What number book is 'I Chronicles' in the King James Bible?

(10) ODD NAME OUT 2: VENGEANCE

▶ Why are these characters seeking 'vengeance'?
▶ Marvel at this question

(11) ELEPHANT DEVICES

▶ EGBDF – something musical
▶ MVEMJSUNP – one-time space set
▶ BYRBG – sporty
▶ GELND – God is a clue!
▶ SHMEO – they're Great
▶ TGCFAOQTCD – this is hard; or about hardness, more properly
▶ CNLMDBC – who is the 'British Commander' they speak of?

(12) HIDDEN FLOWERS

▶ A flower can be pronounced differently...

- ...as a 'flow-er', i.e. a river
- You're looking for hidden rivers in the sentences
- One of the rivers is the Po – congratulations if you managed to spot that without a hint!
- The others begin with C, N, O and T

13 PISCINE PHRASES

- You're looking for hidden water creatures
- The first one is 'bleak'
- The third entry has four hidden in it
- The last two have two each

14 FOUR BY FOUR I

- The first solution is ASAP
- The second is TOPS
- The next three are REPS, EASE, TRAP
- And finally SETT, STAR, TARO
- The top-left letter is S

15 TABLE OF COUNTRIES

- What are the numbers for?
- What sort of table does it refer to?
- Consult the Periodic Table

16 GLOBETROTTING I

- Look for a way to convert each country to a letter sequence
- How might you journey around?

- ▶ Not by plane, but by car
- ▶ Look up international vehicle registrations for each country

(17) KLUMP

- ▶ The 5 goes at the bottom-left
- ▶ The 7 goes at the bottom-right
- ▶ The 12 goes at the top-left

(18) VENN I

- ▶ This is a very shapely question
- ▶ The letters on the left have no curves

(19) ALPHAHUNT

- ▶ One word to find is fraction
- ▶ Two more are viper and squish
- ▶ Also aerobic, jerk, pillow
- ▶ And gnash, text, pretty
- ▶ And something with 'z' at the start

(20) WHO'S NEXT?

- ▶ The first entry is George
- ▶ The second is William
- ▶ The third is Victoria
- ▶ What sequence might this be?

(21) FEATURE

▶ Say them out loud

▶ Which bit don't you say?

(22) WALL TO WALL

▶ The first solution is DUVET

▶ The letters in the squares numbered 2 and 3 are T and H

▶ The letters in the squares numbered 4 and 5 are A and E

▶ The letters in the squares numbered 6 and 7 are R and E

▶ The letter in the square numbered 8 is S

▶ The final solution is STAG

(23) OBSCURE

▶ Think of the weather

▶ Look up, most days

(24) NEXT LINE

▶ It's a lyrical sequence i.e. lyrics from something...

▶ Something seasonal...

▶ ...that is played at Christmas

(25) DOUBLE DUTY NAMES

▶ They are capital cities of which countries?

▶ Why does it say 'names' in the title too?

▶ Some of them are Hungary, Denmark and Pakistan – what do these have in common?

- ▶ And what about Argentina, Rwanda and Bolivia?
- ▶ Look at the ends of the words

(26) IT'S ALL AN ACT
- ▶ You're looking for link words
- ▶ The first is toy
- ▶ The second is story
- ▶ The last one is atlas
- ▶ Once you have the link words, look down the list and what do you see?
- ▶ Does it remind you of anyone's career?
- ▶ What was the title again?

(27) QUESTION
- ▶ What is the title?
- ▶ The title is a massive hint
- ▶ Bits of each word are missing
- ▶ The start and end in fact

(28) EVER-DECREASING CIRCLES
- ▶ There are 100 years in a century
- ▶ And the distance to a target in Olympic archery is 70m
- ▶ L is 50, in Roman numerals
- ▶ Why is 'Cats' Lives' upside down? Maybe the answer is too
- ▶ Each circle corresponds to a different number
- ▶ Trace a path…

- ▶ ...of ever-decreasing value
- ▶ You finish on the bottom-right circle

HINTS FOR CHAPTER 3: TESTING

(I) BOARD

▶ What comes on a board?

▶ What is an 'outstanding' feature?

▶ What could 'outstand' from each line?

▶ It's a cryptic clue to remove a letter from each...

▶ ...and these removed letters can be rearranged to spell another item that fits with the rest

▶ The first letter to remove is 'e'

▶ Then rearrange the letters of 'crud' to make another word

(2) FIVE BY FOUR

▶ Each set is joined in a theme – there is no word play

▶ One set is to do with different shades

▶ Another is to do with a classic arcade game

▶ One is slang terms

▶ Another involves edible things

▶ One of the sets includes INKY and CLYDE

▶ Another involves CHESTNUT and CHOCOLATE

- ▶ A third has PINS and NOODLE

(3) THE MAN WITH THE GOLDEN PUN

- ▶ Can you explain the title?
- ▶ How does it contrast with a more familiar title?
- ▶ What, precisely, has changed?
- ▶ One letter has been altered
- ▶ What movie series does the title (almost) come from?
- ▶ In the first title, what is the word for a female sheep?
- ▶ It is a ewe
- ▶ What is another word for 'solely'?
- ▶ How about 'only'?
- ▶ Can you think of a title that ends with something similar to 'ewes only'?
- ▶ The title described here is 'For Your Ewes Only'...
- ▶ ...which is one letter away from 'For Your Eyes Only'
- ▶ All of the entries clue James Bond movie titles, with a single letter changed

(4) ESCAPED ANIMALS

- ▶ Unusual word choice in the clues often indicates the place an animal should go
- ▶ The first missing animal fits in the middle of 'dolly'
- ▶ The second fits in 'sis'
- ▶ The first missing animal is a lion

- ▶ The second is a zebra
- ▶ The third is a snake
- ▶ The fourth is a camel
- ▶ The fifth is a bear

⑤ DIVERSITY TEST
- ▶ The first is a book by Tom Clancy
- ▶ The second was made into a Kubrick movie
- ▶ What types of word occur in common between the two?
- ▶ So what do you think the sequence is?

⑥ LIFE FORMS
- ▶ Can you find a property that all the first column share?
- ▶ They are all anagrams
- ▶ Then, can you find a property that all the unscrambled words share?

⑦ NEXT IN LINE I
- ▶ The first sequence is out of this world
- ▶ The second is worth counting out
- ▶ The third is ancient
- ▶ The fourth and fifth are both timely

⑧ KEY WORDS
- ▶ The key here is 'key'
- ▶ What types of key can you think of

▶ What about ones you hit with your fingers?

⑨ HOUSE-HUNTING

▶ This puzzle is based on a particular type of advanced cryptic crossword clue called DLM – definition and letter mixture – which you can look up online
▶ 'Wisdom, perhaps' is a clue for the answer in the first sentence, and it refers to a former English actor who was knighted in 2000
▶ 'Roman n' is its letter-mixture anagram
▶ The answer to this is 'Norman'
▶ This sentence then goes on to provide a clue to the next item – the question notes that some sentences contain more than one item
▶ 'given an' is the next letter-mixture anagram
▶ The next straight clue is 'an area of western France'

⑩ WORD ASSOCIATION

▶ What could these numbers refer to?
▶ '41 and 43' is a pretty big clue
▶ What do the letters mean?
▶ The letters indicate changes from the immediate solution to each clue
▶ 'People' refers to 'folk'
▶ The solution to 'savage' is 'fierce'
▶ The solution to 'stream' is 'gush'
▶ You're looking for names of leaders

(11) THEMED PAIRS

▶ Try to make headway by seeking to find the word required by the more precise clues

▶ What could link a plant with orange or yellow heads and a 18th-century Irish dramatist?

▶ Once this pairing has been established, can you find others of a similar type?

▶ The plant is a marigold

▶ The glittering paper is tinsel

(12) MUSICAL WORDS

▶ What is a word for 'came to the throne'?

▶ And 'emotional problems'?

▶ What property do these share?

▶ In what way are they 'musical words'?

▶ What words could you write 'in music'?

▶ Each word has a peculiar property suggested by the title in terms of the range of letters that they use

(13) A BIT TO EAT

▶ The title is key

▶ Read the instructions out loud – do you hear any numbers?

▶ Each row corresponds to a letter

▶ Each letter is made up from 'bits'

▶ A bit is a binary digit

▶ A1... A=1?

14 VENN 2

▶ What is special about the set on the right?

▶ They happen to all be cities, but maybe that's not the key thing about this set

▶ What features are combined in the middle?

15 AUTHORITATIVE COMMENTS

▶ What is missing from each line?

▶ A common type of letter is missing from each line

▶ Who makes 'authoritative comments'? Someone in authority?

▶ They are all quotations, with certain letters removed

16 CLIMBER'S DIVISION

▶ 'Broadcast' is a cryptic way of saying 'sounds like'

▶ The singer is Prince

▶ The British naval college is Dartmouth

17 PERIODIC PAIRS

▶ Periodic refers to time periods

▶ What can these act as prefixes to?

18 BILINGUAL GIBBERISH

▶ The expressions all share two properties

▶ Try using an online translation or search

▶ Each expression represents a different national way of expressing the same sentiment, using the same method

(19) BACK TO THE BEGINNING?

▶ This is a very well-known set, since its members generally hold wide influence

▶ The letters signify the names of people who have occupied a particular position based on a certain aspect of their name

▶ You have to determine which person is missing

(20) LEADERS OF THE GODS

▶ 'Leaders' is a hint to what you're looking for

▶ What is the 'leader' of 'Zeus'?

▶ Who does Zeus correspond to?

▶ Where does -16 come in?

(21) PUNAGRAMS 3

▶ The pun question is very helpful!

▶ The first missing letter is L

▶ The second is A

(22) MISSION ACTIVITY

▶ How might you end up with 'leftovers'?

▶ You need to remove a letter from each

▶ Each word is then anagrammed so that all the resulting words share a common property

(23) NUMBER SEQUENCE

▶ What happened in all those countries?

- ▶ When?
- ▶ Can you find a connection between the when and the number?

(24) TABLE OF CITIES

- ▶ What sort of table is this?
- ▶ How do the numbers connect?
- ▶ You might need a reference to find the answer, before you think of a suitable next item in the list

(25) LANGUAGE TOUR

- ▶ You may need to look up all or most of these online
- ▶ 'Monaco' in Italy does not translate to Monaco in the south of France, but rather to Munich in Germany
- ▶ There is no connection to find here – just a series of trivia

(26) ALAN'S CURIOUS QUEST

- ▶ 'Alan's curious' is a clue – what could 'curious' mean?
- ▶ Try looking up the phrases
- ▶ They are chapter titles in a series of books...
- ▶ ...which has its own chronology
- ▶ Can you convert the books and chapters into coordinates?
- ▶ Plot them on the chart, relative to row 1 and column 1
- ▶ What do you see?

(27) MIDDLESIX

▶ The top-left letter is A, and the bottom-right letter is I

▶ The other corners contain Es

(I) BLETCHLEY PARK CROSSWORD

▶ The clues in this puzzle are solved as in a regular UK cryptic crossword. If you are unfamiliar with the rules and logic of cryptic crosswords then the main thing to bear in mind is that *every* clue includes a definition of the answer – it may be a somewhat misleading definition, but it is always there. The definition always makes up either the start or the end of the clue – never the middle – although it may occasionally also be the entire clue. The non-definition part of the clue is then made up of one or more cryptic indicators, for which you can find many books and online tutorials to explain the rules and logic – and all of the cryptic indicators in the clues in this puzzle are explained in the solutions

▶ The comment about perimeter squares means that the outermost letters on the borders of the grid will spell something (or, in fact, two things) when the puzzle is completed

(2) FLAG TIME

▶ How can flags be used to communicate letters?
▶ And what connection can the time have with the way flags are held?
▶ Look up semaphore

(3) FIRST REVISIONS

▶ There is something very much in common between all the answers
▶ In fact, as the title suggests...
▶ ...only the first letter is revised
▶ You can use this to work out what was going on at 11pm

(4) THE LONG AND SHORT OF IT

▶ The poem tells you exactly what to do
▶ Long words and short words are important
▶ Two-syllable versus one-syllable words specifically
▶ Dits and dahs are terms for dots and dashes...
▶ ...in Morse code

(5) FOUR BY FOUR 2

▶ The first clue is solved as 'HIDE'
▶ And the second as 'WAYS'
▶ In the grid, you need to place a 'C' at top-left
▶ And you need to place a 'S' at bottom-right

(6) NO MAN'S LAND

▶ Is each line roughly the same length? Why might that be?

▶ Do you have the complete alphabet on each line?

▶ What's missing?

(7) MORTPANTEAUX

▶ The title is a big clue

▶ It is a variation of portmanteaux

▶ Although if the title were to be written in the same way as the rest of the clues, it would be just 'ER'

▶ Each entry is written using a consistent logic, rather than being an arbitrary combination

▶ The length of each 'properly spelled' word is given

▶ FOON should be written as SPORK

(8) STEP-BY-STEP

▶ The 'step-by-step' is very important – you need to continually transform what's left in this puzzle

▶ But first of all you need the first step – so can you find a way to read the first line?

▶ Using A=1, B=2, etc you need to break the first line up so it makes sense...

▶ ...and you will need to do the same thing for every line from here on

▶ Line 1 gives you an instruction – so do this to all of the following lines

(9) NEXT IN LINE 2

▶ Each line is a set of initials

▶ One set is pretty to look at; another you can count on; one is something elemental; another is key; and the other is best typed out yourself

(10) KEYWORDS

▶ They are substitutions a machine might make in a certain situation

▶ But not so much nowadays, as it says

▶ On a phone keyboard, are there multiple letters on each number key?

(11) MIXING PAINT

▶ The word 'rails' is in quotes for a reason, and what's this about a fence? You might try doing some research on these words and how they might relate to a hidden message

▶ Why are there 'three' rails, and 'three' paints?

▶ You'll know if you decode the message successfully because you'll end up with three paints – using three rails

▶ Look up 'rail fence cipher'

(12) WAVE DOWN

▶ The strange language in the question is there for a reason

▶ A 'ripest mix-up'? What might that refer to?

- ‘Flag up’ what is happening…
- A ‘cross’ that ‘may be a sign’, with something to ‘calculate’?
- Have a look at the flags for the given countries
- You’re doing flag mathematics
- A ‘ripest’ mix-up is a ‘stripe’ – so stripes are important
- You have three solved examples to demonstrate how the stripes and mathematical operators work

(13) MINI 5×5 JIGSAW

- The text ‘arranged alphabetically in order of their full solution’ is important to note since it will help
- The answers are really short, aren’t they?
- You need to compress each answer in some way to fit to the letter lengths given, as is hinted at by the reference to a ‘full solution’
- The first clue suggests ‘Are you okay?’ – so how would you write that in four letters?
- Spell each answer phonetically using letter pronunciations, so ‘Are you okay?’ becomes RUOK, and so on

(14) TWO BOYS

- Think carefully about the title of each category and its possible significance
- The headings give hints as to how each column is grouped
- There are five members to find – one per row, so each has three clues of three consistent kinds

- ▶ 'Echo' group suggests the use of sound
- ▶ 'Breakdown' group suggests the use of components
- ▶ 'Type' group suggests the use of items as illustrations of the groups to which they might belong
- ▶ For 'tree pitch', think of how you might pronounce the name of a tree and another word meaning pitch
- ▶ For 'award a hectare', think how the phrase could be split into its component parts – an abbreviation for a historic British award, then 'a', and then the abbreviation for hectare
- ▶ For 'Diana', think of what category of things the name might fall into and then think of another name in the same category that tallies with the answer provided by clues in the same row
- ▶ You need to work along each row horizontally to see how each item in the group could be separately defined
- ▶ There is a noted event to which all the answers refer in the same way – the title provides a cryptic hint to its location, although one that will only really provide confirmation once solved
- ▶ 'Tree pitch' is solved as tree=yew and pitch=tar
- ▶ 'Award a hectare' solves to award=OM, a=a and hectare=ha
- ▶ 'Diana' refers to the Roman goddess – so the overall answer for this row is also a Roman goddess

(15) WORD SQUARE

- ▶ For the first property, consider each word carefully and think what three letters could be inserted into each one to form a new word

- ▶ For the second property, work out the way in which each answer is presented and then apply the same treatment to another word that could be defined by the others, once the form of treatment has been deduced
- ▶ For the final property, think of a four-letter answer for the first item and then add another letter each time for subsequent answers – but note that only the first three letters used in each answer are needed
- ▶ The name of the character can be read via a sequence of horizontal and vertical moves in the word square – including on one occasion moving in a reverse direction to revisit a square

(16) OPERATIONS

- ▶ 'The clues also provide openings to an additional hint' is telling you that there's an extra clue written at the start of the clues...
- ▶ ...in the initial letters
- ▶ Each clue is a regular UK-style cryptic crossword clue – see puzzle 1 of this chapter for some general advice on solving cryptic crossword clues
- ▶ The shaded column will spell a thirteenth item of a set of which you will by then already have twelve items, and this thirteenth item is hinted at by the initial letters of the clues

(17) STACKED TIPS

- ▶ Each answer increases in size by one letter, as does the 'remainder of the word that *excludes* the common property'

- ► Each answer shares a very particular property, which should become apparent after you have solved one or two answers
- ► The first clue, like all the rest, consists of a straight clue for the entire answer, and a cryptic clue for the part that *excludes* the common property – there are only two words so there are only two ways to interpret it!
- ► 'Soprano' gives 'S', using a dictionary abbreviation
- ► 'Expert' gives 'hotshot'

(18) TRANSFORMATIONS

- ► A bucket is a pail
- ► Jump is leap, while a bell sound is a peal
- ► Look at the transformation in each case, and associate the transformation with the symbol
- ► A friend is a pal
- ► A force 8 wind is a gale, and a story is a tale
- ► Now apply the same transformations to the words given, one step at a time as shown
- ► There will be multiple ways to do this, but only one way that completes the chain of five commands *and* results in a word that matches one of the given clues

(19) VENN 3

- ► What do these values remind you of?
- ► Something of value perhaps?
- ► They are coin values

▶ They are common coin values in two specific countries

(20) TANGLED TRIOS

▶ The first is to do with Star Trek...
▶ ...and Spock, in particular
▶ While the second is a question of counting it out
▶ Of the remainder, five are triumvirates of characters, and the others refer to a book and to a common phrase

HINTS FOR CHAPTER 5:
ENIGMATIC

(I) ODD PAIR OUT I

▶ The key word here is 'joined' – you will be joining the words into pairs

▶ However, something extra is needed when joining them

▶ An extra letter is needed to join them

▶ But that extra letter differs in some way for one pair

(2) GRIDFILL I

▶ The top-left letter is a 'B'

▶ The bottom-right letter is a 'W'

▶ The top-right letter is an 'I'

▶ And the bottom-left letter is a 'T'

(3) TAKE A LETTER

▶ The 'logical and consistent way' must be fairly specific to give this puzzle a unique answer

▶ You are looking for a way to get from each given word to another that has a very similar meaning

▶ You need to remove a letter...

▶ ...and then solve the anagram of what's left

▶ So, for example, PILFER minus P is an anagram of RIFLE, which has a similar meaning

▶ And then you can apply the same rule to the word you obtain from the removed letters, to get the solution letter

(4) WORD MAESTRO

▶ What language does 'maestro' originate from?

▶ Can you think of English words which have the meanings given?

(5) POP SUMS I

▶ Which artists performed 'Smalltown Boy' and 'More Than In Love'?

▶ The artists in the example are Bronski Beat and Kate Robbins

▶ And what do you notice about those two names?

▶ The names are anagrams of one another

(6) OLD AND NEW

▶ Each word can be replaced with a synonym, or in one case by an abbreviation with the same meaning

▶ Combine the synonyms into pairs that all share the same property. So for example, dawdler and post go together once they have been replaced with their synonyms

▶ Another pair is speechless and movie

▶ Each pair forms a retronym

▶ A retronym is a term for something old that now has to be distinguished from something more recent because it is no longer sufficiently unique. For example, the original version of tennis is now called 'real tennis'

(7) HUNT THE CHARACTER

▶ In the first case for the first component, 'supply… as' functions as an anagram indicator in a cryptic clue – you have to form an anagram of 'free moralist', and the definition is 'a prototype'
▶ In the second case, think of a definite article, plus a word meaning 'peculiarity'
▶ In the third case, look at each of the two words and think of a single common letter that each is missing – and then describe both terms with respect to this
▶ Now find a way to link all three answers to the first component
▶ In the clues for the second component, there is no definition so you have to try to deduce from the wordplay alone how each works
▶ In the first case for the third component, think what the three words might have in common if you remove one letter from each, and what those three letters could form
▶ In the second case, think what word could precede each of the three terms
▶ In the third case, think of two separate synonyms of the key word
▶ Put the four words together and they provide both a clue to the answer as well as an anagram of it

8 VENN 4

- ▶ You'll need to map this one out
- ▶ Specifically, there is a geographical connection within each set
- ▶ Which half of the world is each country in?

9 ISOLATE

- ▶ The middle of the three stars in the left column must have a wall either above or below it...
- ▶ ...although in fact it goes above it
- ▶ The first star in the first row has a wall immediately to its right

10 CRYPTIC MOVIE CLUB

- ▶ AM: this is a word written backwards
- ▶ SCREWABLE: this is one word surrounded by another
- ▶ TAN: the first half of a word
- ▶ VINOUS: two letters and a word
- ▶ KEITH: a word that forms a letter sequence from within part of a title
- ▶ EVOLVE: a word that has been stripped of its outer letters
- ▶ BIG: a word without an abbreviation that can represent a single word

11 TITLE FEATURES

- ▶ Why don't the years match the movies?
- ▶ It's easiest to find the connection if you focus on the shorter titles

- ▶ There isn't much that can be done to or with these shorter titles – so how about removing a single letter (although that won't be sufficient for every title)?
- ▶ There is something hidden in each title
- ▶ Another title is hidden within each given title

(I2) GRIDFILL 2

- ▶ The first row starts with a 'W'
- ▶ And the final row starts with a 'L'
- ▶ The last letter of the third row is a 'Y'
- ▶ And the first letter of the fourth row is an 'E'

(I3) GLOBETROTTING 2

- ▶ They all have the same number of characters, so that can't be it
- ▶ How can the words be 'globetrotting'?
- ▶ Try splitting each word into two halves
- ▶ What does each half represent?

(I4) EVEN MORE TANGLED TRIOS

- ▶ The first are three Stooges
- ▶ The second are needed for good hearing
- ▶ The third is a sandwich
- ▶ The fourth should be sized up
- ▶ The fifth is an elemental band
- ▶ The sixth will completely get you
- ▶ The seventh and eighth are from movie titles

▶ The ninth comes in various phases

15 VENN 5

▶ Think about who would compete in each discipline
▶ Specifically, who might be eligible for each?

16 APT PROPERTY

▶ To be an equation, there is probably something numerical involved
▶ Try replacing the letters with numbers, using A=1, B=2 etc
▶ And split EQUATION into two parts, based on a simple rule, so that each part has the same total value

17 DIGITALLY ENHANCED JIGSAW

▶ The answers are very short – too short to all be regular words, so there must be something else going on
▶ You need to rewrite the solutions in a consistent way before entering them into the grid
▶ How is the puzzle 'digitally enhanced?'
▶ These replacements should sound the same, when each character is pronounced
▶ Characters include letters and digits
▶ For example, MN8 could be 'emanate'
▶ And 'emanate' would solve 'arise'

(18) ODD PAIR OUT 2

▶ One pair is absent and receive
▶ Another pair is bucks and undoes
▶ One more pair is distant and open
▶ Can you find an antonym of each word in each pair?
▶ More than that, can you find a word that works as a single antonym for each pair?

(19) POP SUMS 2

▶ Notice that each sum has four artists on the left and a single artist on the right
▶ Once you have substituted each of the song titles, you should have four words on the left and one word on the right of each equation

(20) ALPHABETIC EXTRACTION

▶ There are three cipher keys, each one word long
▶ Decode each line with each key – but only one key will work for each line
▶ Once you have decoded a line, it will make sense that it matches its original key

(21) GRIDFILL 3

▶ The top-left letter is 'S'
▶ The first line of each shaded area reads 'HC'

(22) FIND THE ACTRESS

▶ Each clue is solved to give a word of the same length

▶ The words need to be connected in some way

▶ Some of the vocabulary is obscure, but can be inferred once you understand how the words connect – so solve as many as you can without spending too long on those you can't yet be sure of

▶ Each solution word is six letters long

▶ You are building a word ladder

(23) CODED TRIBUTE

▶ You'll need to use a keyword cipher

▶ You could experiment with letter frequency analysis and test substitutions to start to untangle the code, or you could take a guess at the keyword phrase – which you will have come across elsewhere in the book

Solutions

Every puzzle has not just a solution, but also an explanation — not just *what* is the answer, but *why* is it the answer? Indeed, for many puzzles if you can't work out what to do, and the hints haven't helped, then try reading just the first part of the solution for an explanation of what's going on, and then return and solve the original puzzle armed with the knowledge of what to do!

(I) FLOWER POWER

Each sentence contains a hidden flower, as follows:

- ▶ Iris: A sparkling diamond for the debona<u>ir is</u> the height of fashion
- ▶ Peony: Skilled jewel-cutters sha<u>pe ony</u>x with tools
- ▶ Lilac: Lapis lazu<u>li lac</u>k the wide range of hues found in other jewels
- ▶ Rose: Eu<u>ros e</u>nable the purchase of German garnets
- ▶ Daisy: A gem-buying agen<u>da is y</u>ielding high profits

(2) MOVIE EDITS

Each entry is an anagram of a well-known movie title.

- ▶ Back to the Future
- ▶ Gone with the Wind
- ▶ Schindler's List
- ▶ Saving Private Ryan
- ▶ Forrest Gump

(3) WORD CONNECTIONS

The words are: FIREARM, ARMBAND, BARMAN, MANKIND and, in the middle, ARMCHAIR and CHAIRMAN.

4 · END OF SERIES

S: the letters are the final letters in each word of the question, 'What is the final letter in this series?'

5 · WHAT THE...?

Each listed entry is the name of a Dickens character with its letters reversed, and all of its vowels removed:

- ▶ Llts = Estella
- ▶ Srggj = Jaggers
- ▶ Skrb = Barkis
- ▶ Tswt = Twist
- ▶ Kcwkcp = Pickwick
- ▶ Hctwgm = Magwitch

Therefore the author – Dickens – becomes Snkcd

6 · CLOCK SCHEDULING

Quarter past seven in the evening. Each word can have 'Battle of' inserted in front of it, and the time then represents the year the battle took place when written using the twenty-four hour clock:

- ▶ 1940 (Battle of Britain)
- ▶ 1815 (Battle of Waterloo)

- ▶ 1945 (Battle of Berlin)
- ▶ 1915 (Battle of Loos)

⑦ COMPLETE THE PICTURE

Each line needs 'ollywood' to be inserted:

- ▶ Dollywood
- ▶ Nollywood
- ▶ Bollywood
- ▶ Hollywood

⑧ PUNAGRAMS I

SPRAIN (pun on sprain and Spain):

- ▶ Belgium (S)
- ▶ Belarus (P)
- ▶ Iceland (R)
- ▶ Slovenia (A)
- ▶ Sweden (I)
- ▶ Serbia (N)

⑨ TETRA-DROP GRID FILL

V	A	C	A	T	E
B	R	I	G	H	T
M	U	F	F	I	N
I	S	L	A	N	D
C	O	F	F	E	E
Z	O	M	B	I	E
S	P	I	D	E	R
C	H	A	R	G	E
B	O	T	T	L	E
S	P	R	I	N	T

(10) QUOTE HANJIE

Those who can imagine anything,
can create the impossible.

(11) ANAGRAM CONNECTIONS I

The connecting word is CROWD since it can be placed before or after each anagrammed entry to make a new word or term:

► CONTROL > crowd control
► OVER > overcrowd
► FUND > crowd-fund
► IN > in-crowd
► PLEASING > crowd-pleasing
► SOURCE > crowdsource
► SURFING > crowd-surfing
► IT > IT crowd
► MADDING > madding crowd

(12) PUNAGRAMS 2

HEALIUM: (pun on heal and helium)

► COPPER (H)
► ARGON (E)
► SILICON (A)
► SODIUM (L)

- ▶ SILVER (I)
- ▶ TIN (U)
- ▶ LEAD (M)

(13) COMMON FEATURES I

They are anagrams of sports:

- ▶ Ice hockey
- ▶ Basketball
- ▶ Triathlon
- ▶ Table tennis
- ▶ Archery
- ▶ Badminton

(14) ODD NAME OUT I

Hugo: These are all movie titles but only Hugo did not win the Academy Award for Best Picture

(15) THE VAULT

Echo; Earl; Elan;
Envy; Exam; Etch;
Ewer; East

(16) WHERE AM I?

The answers are all US states:

- ▶ Tennessee (ten SE)

- ► Illinois (ill in ois)
- ► Rhode Island (road island)
- ► Montana (M on TANA)
- ► New Hampshire (anagram, 'new', of PRIME HASH)
- ► Washington (washing ton)
- ► Pennsylvania (pencil vein ear)
- ► West Virginia (Virginia written 'westwards')
- ► Connecticut (connect i to cut)

(17) COMMON FEATURES 2
They are all words in the English language of Swedish origin

(18) WATCH THIS
Dalmatians: $(47 - 28) \times 12 - 127 = 101$

(19) ALTERNATIVE EXPRESSIONS
- ► A bird in the hand is worth two in the bush
- ► A fate worse than death
- ► Famous for fifteen minutes
- ► A stitch in time saves nine
- ► Cry over spilt milk
- ► Fish out of water

(20) ANAGRAM CONNECTIONS 2
The connecting word is LIFE since it can be placed before or after each anagrammed entry to make a new word or term:

- ► After > afterlife

- ▶ Jacket > life jacket
- ▶ High > high life
- ▶ Time > lifetime
- ▶ Half > half-life
- ▶ Sized > life-sized
- ▶ Blood > lifeblood
- ▶ Family > family life
- ▶ Cycle > life cycle
- ▶ Guard > lifeguard

21 SIX MIX

22 KEY NUMBERS

It would represent a call to the emergency services, 911. The code is the notation on a standard English keyboard: !=1, %=5, ^=6, &=7, *=8, (=9,)=0. Therefore:

- ▶ Ton=100
- ▶ Ice cream with flake=99
- ▶ 1815=Waterloo
- ▶ 007=fictional spy (James Bond)
- ▶ 666=satanic (the devil)

23 CONNECTION

They are all meanings of terms that can be prefixed by 'French'.

- ► French press
- ► French dressing
- ► French leave
- ► French toast
- ► French fries

24 LITERARY SET

They are all literary titles in which the name of a bird is replaced by its respective collective noun:

- ► The Crow Road by Iain Banks
- ► H is for Hawk by Helen Macdonald
- ► The Owl and the Pussycat by Edward Lear
- ► The Maltese Falcon by Dashiell Hammett
- ► The Wings of the Dove by Henry James
- ► Where Eagles Dare by Alistair MacLean
- ► Wild Swans by Jung Chang
- ► Flaubert's Parrot by Julian Barnes
- ► Shroud for a Nightingale by PD James

25 MOVIE CLUB

They are titles of movies in which the name of a US President has been replaced by his successor:

- ► Charlie Wilson's War

- ▶ King Arthur
- ▶ The Truman Show
- ▶ Get Carter
- ▶ Jeremiah Johnson

(26) OBSCENE TITLES

They are titles of movies and books in which a word meaning a shade of blue has been replaced by another:

- ▶ Ocean's Eleven (movie with different versions directed by Lewis Milestone and Steven Soderbergh)
- ▶ Steel Magnolias (movie directed by Herbert Ross)
- ▶ The Royal Tenenbaums (movie directed by Wes Anderson)
- ▶ True Grit (movie with different versions directed by Henry Hathaway and the Coen brothers)
- ▶ Electric Kool-Aid Acid Test (non-fiction book by Tom Wolfe)
- ▶ Alice in Wonderland (children's book by Lewis Carroll)

(27) STRIP SEARCH

I was the indefinite article, A. It is describing a sequence where the word is being 'stripped' each time, losing its first and last letters:

- ▶ PIRATES
- ▶ IRATE
- ▶ RAT
- ▶ A

(28) MUSIC MIX

They are all anagrams of songs which were simultaneous number ones in both the UK and the US. Each entry consists of the song title plus the artist:

- ▶ All About That Bass – Meghan Trainor
- ▶ Grenade – Bruno Mars
- ▶ I Kissed a Girl – Katy Perry
- ▶ SexyBack – Justin Timberlake
- ▶ Viva la Vida – Coldplay
- ▶ Shape of You – Ed Sheeran
- ▶ I Will Always Love You – Whitney Houston

(29) GEM OF A PUZZLE

A stone – stones are used in curling; a stone = 14 pounds; to stone is to punish; stones are on the ground; kidney stones are painful; and the title 'gem' hints at a gemstone

(30) CAPITAL LETTERS

These clues represent hyphenated words:

- ▶ B-movie
- ▶ U-turn
- ▶ D-Day
- ▶ A-lister
- ▶ P-trap
- ▶ E-layer
- ▶ S-bahn
- ▶ T-shirt

The initial letters spell out a capital, BUDAPEST

SOLUTIONS FOR CHAPTER 2: COMPUTABLE

(I) PIVOT POINTS

Each word can be mirrored to form a palindrome. The final letter of the original three-letter word acts as a pivot point:

- ▶ Madam
- ▶ Rotor
- ▶ Tenet
- ▶ Dewed
- ▶ Sagas
- ▶ Level

(2) HOLY ORDERS

They are anagrams of the first five books of the Old Testament. Solving the anagrams, and then placing the books in order, gives:

- ▶ Genesis
- ▶ Exodus
- ▶ Leviticus
- ▶ Numbers
- ▶ Deuteronomy

Against the original entries, this corresponds to 4, 3, 5, 1, 2

MAN TO MAN

The sequences are as follows:

- ▶ ROB > MUG > FOOL > JOSH
- ▶ PAT > TAP > BUG > MIDGE
- ▶ NICK > JAIL > CAN > JOHN
- ▶ MARK > SPOT > NOTICE > BILL

(4) **A NEW TERM**

Take the first letter of each digit when written as a word, to spell: SENTTEENSOFFTOETON, which can be broken up to read 'Sent teens off to Eton'. In other words, the children were sent to the famous private school, Eton.

(5) **CAN YOU CONNECT**

They are things you can draw

(6) **ROUTE SUM**

The common denominator in the dates of these events is 66, since they are events that occurred in chronological order of centuries from 1066 to 1966 inclusive. The sum of the remaining component in their dates is therefore 145 (10 + 11 + 12 + 13 + 14 + 15 + 16 + 17 + 18 + 19). The title is an oblique reference to the celebrated Route 66, the highway that crosses a large part of the United States.

⑦ NAVIGRID

⑧ SO IT BEGINS (AND ENDS)

Each word starts and ends with the same two letters:

- ▶ CHURCH
- ▶ INSULIN
- ▶ HEADACHE
- ▶ EMBLEM
- ▶ ESCAPES
- ▶ MAGMA
- ▶ ETHERNET
- ▶ DECIDE
- ▶ PHOTOGRAPH
- ▶ NECKLINE

(9) MISFORTUNE

They are the 13th member of noted groups:

▶ 13th US President
▶ Traditional 13th wedding anniversary symbol
▶ 13th book of the Bible (King James Version)
▶ The area of the Moon that was the target of the failed Apollo 13 mission in 1970
▶ 13th amendment of the US constitution
▶ Putative 13th sign of the zodiac

(10) ODD NAME OUT 2: VENGEANCE

Scott. These are all first names of Marvel superheroes, but Scott (Lang, Ant-Man) is not an Avenger in the first film.

(11) ELEPHANT DEVICES

▶ The five lines of the treble clef in music: E, G, B, D, F
▶ Order of the planets in proximity to the sun (until Pluto was declassified as a planet): Mercury, Venus, Earth, Mars, Jupiter, Saturn, Uranus, Neptune, Pluto
▶ The hues of the five official Olympic rings: blue, yellow, red, black and green
▶ The first five books of the Bible, known as the Pentateuch: Genesis, Exodus, Leviticus, Numbers, Deuteronomy
▶ The five Great Lakes in decreasing size of their surface area: Superior, Huron, Michigan, Erie and Ontario

- The Mohs scale of mineral hardness on a scale of 1-10: talc, gypsum, calcite, fluorite, apatite, orthoclase, quartz, topaz, corundum, diamond
- The actors who have played James Bond, in chronological order of appearance in terms of the initial in their surname: Sean Connery, David Niven, George Lazenby, Roger Moore, Timothy Dalton, Pierce Brosnan, Daniel Craig

(12) HIDDEN FLOWERS

There are five rivers ('flowers' – i.e. 'flow-ers') hidden in the text as follows:

- Po
- Cam
- Nile
- Ouse
- Tagus

Their positions are highlighted here:

Kew Gardens is a beloved place to sto**p o**ff to see flowers from across the world. It always provides fantasti**c am**usement to see the exotic names and variety of species. There have been many new ones placed into the collectio**n, I le**arn. Even the most zeal**ous e**nthusiast for flowers would have his or her interest satisfied. One can find useful information everywhere and some people concoc**t a gus**hing tribute at the end of their visit.

(13) PISCINE PHRASES

The names of thirteen individual sea creatures are hidden in the statements:

- ▶ It's supporta**ble a k**ing shoul**d ab**dicate when under pressure.
- ▶ There's no desire in the general population for a long-forgot**ten ch**urch
- ▶ **T**oys **ter**med intelligenc**e el**ements are develope**d or y**et to be used in ot**her ring**s for spying operations
- ▶ Tourists es**cape lin**es in busy coastal port
- ▶ The lack of foreign languages in British education is a basi**c od**dity
- ▶ People sto**p out**side for drink**able t**reats.
- ▶ All kinds of money e**manate e**asily from a ri**ch ar**istocrat

(14) FOUR BY FOUR I

The solution words, and the corresponding filled grid, are as follows:

- ▶ ASAP
- ▶ TOPS
- ▶ REPS
- ▶ EASE
- ▶ TRAP
- ▶ SETT
- ▶ STAR
- ▶ TARO

S	T	A	R
E	A	S	E
T	R	A	P
T	O	P	S

(15) TABLE OF COUNTRIES

Fiji (9), or any other country beginning with the letter 'F'. The initial letter in each case conforms to consecutive elements in the Periodic Table, with their corresponding atomic numbers:

- ▶ Carbon (C)
- ▶ Nitrogen (N)
- ▶ Oxygen (O)
- ▶ Fluorine (F)

(16) GLOBETROTTING I

Once represented as international car registrations, the countries spell out the answers to the questions:

- ▶ MALTA. Countries visited: Morocco (MA), Lithuania (LT), Austria (A)
- ▶ PERU. Countries visited: Portugal (P), Spain (E), Burundi (RU)
- ▶ IRAQ. Countries visited: Italy (I), Argentina (RA), Qatar (Q)
- ▶ I WANT TO TRAVEL FOR AGES. Countries visited: Italy (I), Nigeria (WAN), Thailand (T) Tonga (TO), Turkey (TR), Austria (A), Vatican City (V), Spain (E), Luxembourg (L), Faroes (FO), Argentina (RA), Georgia (GE), Sweden (S)

(17) KLUMP

(18) VENN I

Left set: letters made from straight lines

Right set: letters made from curved lines

Intersection: letters with both straight and curved lines

(19) ALPHAHUNT

The letter D:

Words to find: fraction; viper; squish; aerobic; jerk; pillow; gnash; text; pretty; zoom

20 WHO'S NEXT?

Taylor, Hurley, or any famous person called Elizabeth. These are the most recent British monarchs from 1820 onwards: George, William, Victoria, Edward, George, Edward, George and then Elizabeth.

21 FEATURE

All the words include a silent letter 't'

22 WALL TO WALL

The diagonal spells DYNAMO:

23 OBSCURE

A cloud. It's made of water and often returns it as rain. You back up data to a cloud. And as per the title, to obscure is to cloud.

24 NEXT LINE

APIAPT. The sequence is lines from the song 'The Twelve Days of Christmas', as follows:

- ▶ 5 Gold Rings
- ▶ 4 Calling Birds
- ▶ 3 French Hens
- ▶ 2 Turtle Doves
- ▶ A Partridge In A Pear Tree

25 DOUBLE DUTY NAMES

Bamako. The names of the countries to which four of the cities belong (Greece, Hungary, Denmark, Pakistan) end with a boy's name, while those of four others (Argentina, Rwanda, Canada, Bolivia) end with a girl's name. The name with which the remaining country (Mali) ends is both a boy's and a girl's name.

26 IT'S ALL AN ACT

Tom Hanks. The central letters spell the names of movies he has starred in: Toy Story, Big, Saving Private Ryan, Cloud Atlas:

- ▶ Cuddly toy – toy poodle
- ▶ Fairy story – story teller
- ▶ Think big – big apple
- ▶ Energy saving – saving grace
- ▶ In private – private investigator
- ▶ Meg Ryan – Ryan Gosling
- ▶ Storm cloud – cloud nine
- ▶ Road atlas – Atlas mountains

27 QUESTION

As suggested by the title, they are all question words. Each word is missing its first and last letter. The anagrams are marked with an asterisk:

▶ WHO * (or WHY)
▶ WHY (or WHO *)
▶ WHAT
▶ WHEN
▶ WHERE
▶ HOW *

28 EVER-DECREASING CIRCLES

Solve the clue in each circle to give a different value. The path is then 'ever-decreasing' from the start to the lowest value, as shown:

▶ 'Days in four months' refers to the fact that there are four months that all have the same number of days, 30

SOLUTIONS FOR CHAPTER 3: TESTING

(I) BOARD

They are anagrams of types of cheese with an extra letter. The extra letters can then be arranged to form CHUTNEY, a possible accompaniment to cheese. The cheeses are:

► Curd (e)
► Feta (c)
► Brie (t)
► Edam (n)
► Danbo (u)
► Stilton (y)
► Pecorino (h)

(2) FIVE BY FOUR

The sets are:

► Pac-Man ghosts: BLINKY, PINKY, CLYDE and INKY
► Apples: FUJI, JAZZ, DISCOVERY and RUSSET
► Types of sweet: BOILED, CHEWY, FIZZY and SOUR
► Shades of brown: TAN, FAWN, CHOCOLATE and CHESTNUT
► Slang for parts of the body: PINS, HOOTER, MUG and NOODLE

(3) THE MAN WITH THE GOLDEN PUN

Like the title to the puzzle, each motion picture is the name of an actual Bond movie but with one letter changed. The movies are:

- ▶ For your ewes only (For Your Eyes Only)
- ▶ Licence to bill (Licence to Kill)
- ▶ Tomorrow never lies (Tomorrow Never Dies)
- ▶ A view to a hill (A View to a Kill)
- ▶ The world is hot enough (The World is Not Enough)
- ▶ Die another May (Die Another Day)
- ▶ Casino Royals (Casino Royale)
- ▶ Er, no (Dr No)
- ▶ You only jive twice (You Only Live Twice)

(4) ESCAPED ANIMALS

The animals, and the restored sentences, are as follows:

- ▶ Lion: It's the dol<u>l l on</u>ly used to play with my friend
- ▶ Zebra: Which si<u>ze bra</u>s are stocked in the lingerie department?
- ▶ Snake: Hear<u>s nake</u>d woman putting on clothes after bathing
- ▶ Camel: Male be<u>came l</u>ast to finish the race, having fallen first
- ▶ Bear: Is a bul<u>b ear</u>ly to rise from their bed in the spring?

(5) DIVERSITY TEST

The sequence consists of the initials of book titles which contain different shades by their respective authors, the length of whose names are given. The books are given in the order of the of their appearance in the rainbow: red, orange, yellow, green, blue, indigo and violet. Violet therefore has to be deduced. The title hints at the use of the rainbow as a symbol for diversity.

The book titles are:

- ▶ The Hunt for Red October by Tom Clancy
- ▶ A Clockwork Orange by Anthony Burgess
- ▶ Crome Yellow by Aldous Huxley
- ▶ Anne of Green Gables by Lucy Maud Montgomery
- ▶ Porterhouse Blue by Tom Sharpe
- ▶ Indigo by Alice Hoffman
- ▶ Any book with 'violet' in the title will work here, such as Shrinking Violet by Lou Kuenzler (3,8)

(6) LIFE FORMS

The transformation from the first to the second column is to find an anagram of the word; then from the second to third column it is to find a homophone of the word. The third column consists solely of animals:

DOTE	TOED	TOAD
ROBE	BORE	BOAR
KILNS	LINKS	LYNX
ASHORE	HOARSE	HORSE
DARE	DEAR	DEER
TEACHER	CHEATER	CHEETAH

(7) NEXT IN LINE I

Each list is a sequence of either initials or letters as follows:

▶ U: Mercury Venus Earth Mars Jupiter Saturn **Uranus** (planets in our solar system)

▶ S: first second third fourth fifth sixth **seventh**

▶ M: I (1) V (5) X (10) L (50) C (100) D (500) **M (1000)** – Roman numerals in increasing value

▶ S: March April May June July August **September**

▶ T: Friday Saturday Sunday Monday Tuesday Wednesday **Thursday**

(8) KEY WORDS

They are words that can be spelled exclusively with either the left-hand or the right-hand side of a QWERTY keyboard, respectively

(9) HOUSE-HUNTING

They are the royal houses of England and Great Britain:

▶ Norman (Wisdom, perhaps; anagram: Roman n)

▶ Angevin (area of western France; anagram: given an)

▶ Plantagenet (Latin sprig of broom; anagram: get plate ann)

▶ Lancaster (bomber; anagram: clear stan)

▶ York (bowl; anagram: ry – ok)

▶ Tudor (architectural style; anagram: tour d)

▶ Stuart (Little, perhaps; anagram: a trust)

▶ Orange (fruit; anagram: on grea)

▶ Hanover (German city; anagram: hear nov)

▶ Windsor (Barbara, maybe; anagram: in words)

This leaves Saxe-Coburg-Gotha as the missing royal house.

(10) WORD ASSOCIATION

A poorly dressed woman. The numbers represent the sequence number of US presidents and the words give definitions of their names with the initial letters switched to the letter given in brackets:

▶ 11 = folk/Polk

▶ 14 = fierce/Pierce

▶ 18 = orant/Grant

▶ 27 = daft/Taft

▶ 29 = warding/Harding

▶ 38 = cord/Ford

▶ 39 = barter/Carter

▶ 41 and 43 = gush/Bush Senior or Junior

▶ 45 = frump/Trump

(11) THEMED PAIRS

The four pairs comprise meanings of words that begin or end with the name of a particular metal. Therefore the pairs must be selected as follows:

▶ Starring/implore = leading/plead

▶ Glittering paper/swift-flying songbird = tinsel/martin

- De-creasing/firedog = ironing/andiron
- 18th century Irish dramatist/flower with yellow or orange heads = Goldsmith/marigold

(12) MUSICAL WORDS

They are words that consist entirely of letters that represent musical notes – A, B, C, D, E, F, G:

- Acceded
- Baggage
- Cabbage
- Defaced
- Effaced
- Facade
- Gagged

(13) A BIT TO EAT

Each of the ticks can be read as a '1' in a binary number, with the absence of a tick representing a '0'. A single binary digit is called a 'bit', thus the title of the puzzle. The puzzle also refers to the values of the form 2^x that are the decimal equivalent of a binary digit: $2^0 = 1$ = 'one', $2^1 = 2$ = 'too', $2^2 = 4$ = 'for', $2^3 = 8$ = 'ate', $2^4 = 16$ = 'six teen'-agers.

The orders are shown converted to decimal in this table:

	Apple pie 16	Ice cream 8	Burger 4	Fries 2	Drink 1	Total value
Anne		✓				8
Barney		✓	✓	✓	✓	15
Coleen	✓		✓			20
David			✓			4
Erica		✓	✓	✓	✓	15
Frank			✓	✓	✓	7

The question refers to the 'A1 Cafe', which is a hint that A=1. Continuing with B=2, C=3 and so on, the values can then be converted into letters: 8=H, 15=O, 20=T, 4=D, 15=O, 7=G.

So the missing item was a HOTDOG.

14 VENN 2

Left set: Countries

Right set: Five-letter words

Intersection: Five-letter countries

15 AUTHORITATIVE COMMENTS

They are all sayings or excerpts of speeches made by US presidents with the vowels removed, and the spaces rearranged:

▶ Read my lips: no new taxes – slogan used by George H W Bush
▶ The only thing we have to fear is fear itself – broadcast by Franklin D Roosevelt

- My fellow Americans! Ask not what your country can do for you. Ask what you can do for your country – speech by John F Kennedy
- I never trust a man unless I've got his pecker in my pocket – comment by Lyndon B Johnson
- If you want a friend in Washington, get a dog – comment attributed to Harry S Truman
- Blessed are the young for they shall inherit the national debt – Herbert Hoover
- You may fool all the people some of the time; you can even fool some of the people all the time; but you can't fool all of the people all the time – speech by Abraham Lincoln

(16) CLIMBER'S DIVISION

The noted group are members of the Ivy League – hence the 'Climber's Division' title. The members of the group given by each clue in turn are as follows:

- Brown (in Rhode Island) – UK Prime Minister, Gordon Brown
- Columbia (in New York) – homophone ('broadcast') of Colombia, South American country
- Cornell (in New York state) – former US grunge musician, Chris Cornell
- Dartmouth (in New Hampshire) – British naval college
- Pennsylvania (in Pennsylvania) – reference to the Pennsylvania Dutch
- Princeton (in New Jersey) – Prince (singer) + ton (weight)

▶ Yale (in Connecticut) – key supplier

Harvard (in Massachusetts) is therefore the missing member of the group

(17) PERIODIC PAIRS

The items are prefixes to different days of the week, denoting events in the religious, sporting and social calendar:

▶ Cyber and Plough for Monday
▶ Shrove and Super for Tuesday
▶ Ash and Spy for Wednesday
▶ Black and Maundy for Thursday
▶ Casual and Good for Friday
▶ Holy and Lazarus for Saturday
▶ Bloody and Palm for Sunday

(18) BILINGUAL GIBBERISH

They are ways of saying something is unintelligible in a different language, and furthermore each compares with a foreign language to do so:

▶ It looks like Chinese (in Filipino)
▶ It's Arabic for me (in Italian)
▶ It's Volapuk to me (in Esperanto)
▶ It's Chinese (in French).

The equivalent phrase used in English would be 'it's all Greek to me', or perhaps 'double Dutch', as suggested cryptically by the title.

19) BACK TO THE BEGINNING?

The numbers correspond to the lengths of US presidential surnames. The only other ten-letter surname of a US president is George WASHINGTON – hence the title 'Back to the Beginning?' So the correct letter to write in is 'W':

- ▶ 4: Bush × 2 (HW + W), Ford, Polk, Taft
- ▶ 5: Adams × 2 (John + Quincy), Grant, Hayes, Nixon, Obama, Trump + Tyler
- ▶ 6: Arthur, Carter, Hoover, Monroe, Pierce, Reagan, Taylor + Truman, Wilson
- ▶ 7: Clinton, Harding, Jackson + Johnson × 2 (Andrew + LBJ), Kennedy, Lincoln, Madison
- ▶ 8: Buchanan, Coolidge, Fillmore, Garfield, Harrison × 2 (Benjamin + William), McKinley, Van Buren
- ▶ 9: Cleveland, Jefferson, Roosevelt × 2 (Theodore + FDR)
- ▶ 10: Eisenhower, Washington

20) LEADERS OF THE GODS

The translation in question is between the Greek name for the god and their Roman name. As the title of the puzzle ('leaders') indicates, the first letter of the name is the relevant one: the number represents how to get from the first letter of the Greek name to the first letter of the Roman name alphabetically.

Therefore, since the Roman name for Dionysus is Bacchus, and 'B' is two letters before 'D' alphabetically, then Dionysus = -2

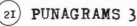

21 PUNAGRAMS 3

The sports, and their added letters, are as follows:

- ▶ GOLF (L)
- ▶ ARCHERY (A)
- ▶ SOCCER (C)
- ▶ BASKETBALL (K)
- ▶ SNOOKER (R)
- ▶ SUMO (O)
- ▶ WRESTLING (S)
- ▶ SQUASH (S)

This spells out 'LACK ROSS', which is a pun on lacrosse and the TV show 'Friends'.

22 MISSION ACTIVITY

Each word consists of an anagram of a word meaning 'spy', being either a synonym or a real or fictional example of a spy, plus an extra letter. The extra letters left can then be rearranged to form the word ESPIONAGE:

- ▶ PLANT (+i)
- ▶ NARK (+o)
- ▶ MOLE (+n)
- ▶ AGENT (+e)
- ▶ SLEEPER (+s)

- ▶ TOUT (+p)
- ▶ INFORMER (+g)
- ▶ STEED (+a) – John Steed was the suave, bowler-hatted character played by Patrick Macnee in the UK TV series 'The Avengers'
- ▶ BLUNT (+e) – Anthony Blunt was the British art historian and Surveyor of the Queen's Pictures who was publicly unveiled in 1979 as a former agent of the Soviet Union

(23) NUMBER SEQUENCE

The next item in the sequence would be 9 = Rio de Janiero. The sequence is Olympic host cities in chronological order with the sum of the digits in the dates of the Olympic games:

- ▶ Sydney in 2000 = 2 + 0 + 0 + 0 = 2
- ▶ Athens in 2004 = 2 + 0 + 0 + 4 = 6
- ▶ Beijing in 2008 = 2 + 0 + 0 + 8 = 10
- ▶ London in 2012 = 2 + 0 + 1 + 4 = 5
- ▶ Rio de Janeiro in 2016 = 2 + 0 + 1 + 6 = 9

(24) TABLE OF CITIES

Bristol (35 ie Br for Bromine), or any city beginning with 'Br'. The first two letters of each city conform to the following consecutive elements in the Periodic Table with their corresponding atomic numbers:

- ▶ Gallium (Ga)
- ▶ Germanium (Ge)
- ▶ Arsenic (As)

- ▶ Selenium (Se)
- ▶ Bromine (Br)

(25) LANGUAGE TOUR

They are the names of foreign cities in the language of the country indicated in brackets:

- ▶ Mailand (Germany) refers to Milan in Italy
- ▶ Monaco (Italy) refers to Munich in Germany
- ▶ Aix-la-Chapelle (France) refers to Aachen in Germany
- ▶ Rijsel (Holland) refers to Lille in France
- ▶ Wien (Germany) refers to Vienna in Austria
- ▶ Bryste (Wales) refers to Bristol in England
- ▶ Ginebra (Spain) refers to Geneva in Switzerland
- ▶ Pressburg (Germany) refers to Bratislava in Slovakia

(26) ALAN'S CURIOUS QUEST

The clues are chapter titles from the Chronicles of Narnia books. Taking the books in chronological (rather than publication) order, these act as coordinates on the map. For example, 'Lucy Looks into a Wardrobe' is Book 2 Chapter 1, which represents the square in the second column and first row up, as indicated by the '1's at the bottom-left of the grid.

When all the squares with listed chapters are shaded, the word 'Lion.' is spelled out when the page is turned through 90 degrees, as shown below. This answer is also hinted at by the title of the puzzle, 'Alan's Curious Quest' – 'curious' is an anagram indicator, and an anagram of 'Alan's' is 'Aslan', the name of the lion in the Narnia series.

(27) **MIDDLESIX**

	W	S	B	
P	A	C	E	D
S	T	A	F	F
P	E	R	I	L
	R	E	T	

(I) BLETCHLEY PARK CROSSWORD

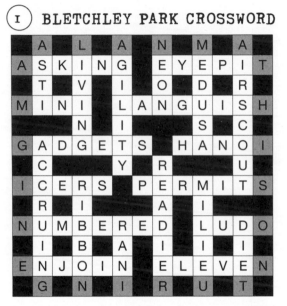

The perimeter letters of the crossword from the top left-hand corner read in a clockwise direction ALAN MATHISON TURING ENIGMA.

Following is an explanation of how the cryptic part of each of the clues works. In 1-down, '& lit.' refers to a clue where the entire clue does double duty as both a cryptic clue *and* definition.

Across

7. ASKING = As king (in a ruling capacity)

8. EYE-PIT = Homophone of 'I Pitt' (personal declaration by ex-PM, William Pitt)

9. MINI = MI (military intelligence) + NI (Northern Ireland = province)

10. LANGUISH = L (learner) + anguish (suffering)

11. GADGETS = (Lo)g(ic) + anagram of staged

13. HANOI = H (hotel in NATO phonetic alphabet) + a + no 1 (top)

14. ICERS = (D)icers (people who take risks)

17. PERMITS = IT (modern technology) in perms (waves)

19. NUMBERED = Numb (inactive) + ere (before) + d

21. LUDO = L (lecturer) + u (university) + do (note)

23. ENJOIN = E + n (last letters) + join (connect)

24. ELEVEN = Double definition: eleven=team (side)/number of letters in the word 'cryptograph'

Down

1. ASTI = Hidden in (Veron)a's ti(pple) '&lit.' clue

2. LIVING = Liv(e) (not recorded) + in + G (government)

3. AGILITY = GI (serviceman) + lit (fired) in a(genc)y (outsiders in agency)

4. NEON = Hidden in (machi)ne on(ly)

5. MEDUSA = Med (sea) + USA (home of the CIA)

6. AIR SCOUT = A1 (capital) + anagram of court's

12. ACCRUING = Homophone of a crewing (a manning of operations)

14. READIER = Die (stop) in rear (back)
16. RIBBON = Double definition; ribbon = fine material in bands/ part of typewriter
18. MILIEU = M (spymaster) + I (independent) + lieu (place)
20. RANI = Iran (country) with I at bottom (leader's demoted)
22. DIET = i.e. (that is) in initial letters of decoding team

(2) FLAG TIME

If the times are interpreted as hands on an analogue clock, and then read as semaphore ('flag time'), then the times would spell out TRIBAND – the type of flag asked for in the question.

(3) FIRST REVISIONS

Answer: I was having clothes on (or eroding, or anything else that equates to WEARING). With the indexed letter of the alphabet (1am = 0100 hours = A, 2am = 0200 hours = B, ..., 1pm = 1300hrs = M, etc), plus 'earing', I was:

▶ 2am: BEARING
▶ 6am: FEARING
▶ 7am: GEARING
▶ 8am: HEARING
▶ 2pm: NEARING
▶ 6pm: REARING
▶ 7pm: SEARING
▶ 8pm: TEARING
▶ 11pm: WEARING

(4) THE LONG AND SHORT OF IT

If you take a one-syllable word as a dot (or 'dit') and a two-syllable word as a dash (or 'dah'), then each line spells a letter in Morse code: '-.. / .- / ... / .... / .. / -. / --.' This equates to DASHING – which is how Morse could be both 'running' and 'handsome'.

(5) FOUR BY FOUR 2

The solution words, and the corresponding filled grid, are as follows:

► HIDE
► WAYS
► RIGA
► CHOW
► OGLE
► BEES
► IDLY
► CRIB

C	R	I	B
H	I	D	E
O	G	L	E
W	A	Y	S

NO MAN'S LAND

These are sets of letters of the alphabet with letters removed, and the letters removed are then anagrammed to reveal:

- ▶ MEXICO
- ▶ HONDURAS
- ▶ DENMARK
- ▶ UZBEKISTAN
- ▶ SWITZERLAND
- ▶ HUNGARY
- ▶ FRANCE
- ▶ SLOVENIA
- ▶ VIETNAM
- ▶ BELARUS

7 MORTPANTEAUX

These are portmanteaux that are the other way around to normal, as indicated by the title. Each word is constructed from the letters not used by the correct portmanteaux:

- ▶ PARIONETTE: MUPPET
- ▶ ROLETUME: COSPLAY
- ▶ HOMBAY: BOLLYWOOD
- ▶ FOON: SPORK
- ▶ POMERINE: TANGELO
- ▶ LEAKFAST: BRUNCH
- ▶ FOKE: SMOG

- CAMFORD: OXBRIDGE
- EGANTIC: GINORMOUS
- BIDEO: VLOG

(8) STEP-BY-STEP

The first line, if you use A=1, ... Z=26, decodes to DIVIDE NEXT LINES BY THREE, once you have split the numbers up as follows:

- 4 9 22 9 4 5 14 5 24 20 12 9 14 5 19 2 25 20 8 18 5 5

Applying the instruction to the next line in particular obtains:

- 18 5 22 5 18 19 5 14 5 24 20 12 9 14 5 19

If you then apply A=1, ... Z=26 again then the second line reads REVERSE NEXT LINES. Dividing the third line by three gives:

- 41502 11312 541921 242541 81191513

If this is then reversed you obtain:

- 3 1 5 19 1 18 14 5 24 2 12 9 14 5 2 1 3 11 20 5 14

...which translates to CAESAR NEXT LINE BACK TEN, indicating that we should apply a Caesar shift to the final line.

So if you take the last line and divide by three:

- 3913528162252321145132 391 251734211 51814

...and reverse it:

▶ 4 18 15   11 24 3 7 15 2   19 3
23 15 4 11 23 25 2 26 18 25 3 19 3

▶ DRO KXCGOB SC WODKWYBZRYCSC

…and then Caesar-shift it as described to reveal THE ANSWER IS METAMORPHOSIS

(9) NEXT IN LINE 2

Each list is a sequence of either initials or letters as follows:

▶ S: one two three four five six seven
▶ R: violet indigo blue green yellow orange red
▶ Z: M N B V C X Z (bottom row of a keyboard in reverse order)
▶ N: hydrogen helium lithium beryllium boron carbon nitrogen (elements in increasing atomic number)
▶ F: C G D A E B F# (major keys in increasing order of number of sharps)

(10) KEYWORDS

When using standard predictive text messaging, keying in BARMAID, SMIRNOFF and PINT typically produces CARNAGE, POISONED and SHOT – try it on an old phone!

11

MIXING PAINT

The words 'rails' and 'fence' hint at using a 'rail fence' cipher, and the repeated reference to 'three' indicates that the cipher should have three rails.

In a rail fence cipher, the plain text is written downwards and diagonally on successive 'rails' of an imaginary fence, then moving up and diagonally when reaching the bottom rail. When the top rail is reached again, the same is then repeated until the entire text is written out. The message is then read in rows, left-to-right and top-to-bottom.

Putting the given text into the 'rail fence' cipher with a key of three gives:

P			L			A			T			W	
	U		P	E	C	R		E	B	O		N	
		R			S			L			R		

So the solution is purple, scarlet, brown.

12

WAVE DOWN

Each country should be converted to its flag, as hinted at by the title and 'flag up'. Each line should be interpreted as an equation with mathematical signs ('sign'), such as a multiplication sign ('cross') or addition operator. Also, 'ripest mix-up' is an anagram indicator for 'stripes', to indicate that you should count the number of stripes to find a number. Therefore the aim of the puzzle is to interpret the flags as mathematical equations.

With this conversion, the clues read:

▶ 3 × 2 = 6
▶ 5 + 3 = 8
▶ 13 × 0 = 0

So the final line reads 3 + 3, and the answer therefore is 6.

(I3) MINI 5×5 JIGSAW

Each answer must be written phonetically using letter pronunciations, as follows:

Across:

1.   Intense watch = Beady eye (BDI)
3.   Understand = See why (CY)
5.   Cockney greeting = 'ello (LO)

6. Monkey = Titi (TT)

8. Is there a problem? = Are you okay? (RUOK)

10. Void = Empty (MT)

11. Power = Energy (NRG)

13. Here in France = Ici ('here' in French) (EC)

14. Sweetheart = Cutie (QT)

Down:

1. Netanyahu = Bibi (BB\)

2. You've done me a favour = I owe you (IOU)

4. Palish = Whitey (YT)

6. Spanish relative = Tio ('uncle' in Spanish) (TO)

7. Tropical resin = Elemi (LME)

8. Bohemian = RT (RT)

9. Secretive = Cagey (KG)

11. Jealousy = Envy (NV)

12. Disagree = Argue (RQ)

(14) TWO BOYS

The members of the group are the names given to the beaches in the D-Day landings in Normandy on June 5th 1944. They are Utah, Omaha, Gold, Juno and Sword. Each is referred to in three ways:

▶ Homophonically – 'Echo' group: yew tar, Omagh haar, goaled, Juneau, sord

▶ As a breakdown of their components – 'Breakdown' group: ut (archaic word for 'as')+a\h, OM+a+ha, go+ld, Jun+o, s+word

► As associative hints – 'Type' group: another US state, another city in Nebraska, another precious metal, another Roman goddess, another weapon

The title hints to the components of Normandy as Norm + Andy (two boys).

(15) WORD SQUARE

The answers to the three questions are:

► LAN can be inserted into each word to form another word: coLANder, pLANet, seaLANt, sLANting
► The real word NIT is a reversal of TIN – all the other words are reversals of meanings of tin: CAN, METAL, MONEY, PLATE
► GRU forms the first three letters: GRUb (food), GRUff (rough), GRUnge (US rock music), GRUmble (complaint)

Putting LAN, NIT and GRU into the grid gives:

L	A	N
N	I	T
G	R	U

The name ALAN TURING can then be read by moving horizontally and vertically from letter to letter:

(16) OPERATIONS

The thirteen items are code names for Western military operations during the Second War. They are as follows:

1. Michaelmas (US amphibious operation in New Guinea, 1944) – anagram of AIM with MALES around CH

2. Avalanche (Allied invasion of Italy, 1943) – A N CH (Switzerland) in A VALE

3. Overlord (Battle of Normandy in the D-Day landings, 1944) – OVER + LORD

4. Corkscrew (Allied invasion of Pantelleria, 1943) – CORK'S CREW

5. Mincemeat (British disinformation strategy, 1943) – anagram of NICE TEAM ('cooked') after M

6. Cactus (Battle of Guadalcanal, 1942) – CT in CA US

7. Ringbolt (US seizure of Solomon Islands, 1942) – anagram of TROUBLING - U (not 'for all to see')

8. Buffalo (Allied breakout from Anzio, 1944) – double definition

9. Reservist (Allied operation to seize Oran in Algeria, 1942) –

double definition

10. Teardrop (US operation to sink U-boats off the eastern US coast, 1945) – DROP after anagram of TEAR

11. Lumberjack (US operation to capture the west bank of the Rhine, 1945) – LUMBER plus JACK

12. Grenade (Allied operation to cross the Roer river, 1945) – anagram of GRANDEE

The final one to be deduced, in the highlighted column, is Market Garden (Allied airborne and ground operation to encircle the Ruhr, 1944), further hinted at by the initial letters of clues in order: (A) BRIDGE TOO FAR, the title of the book and movie by Cornelius Ryan dealing with the operation.

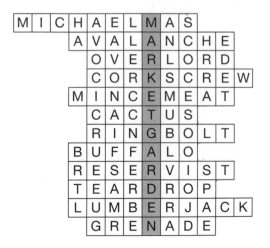

17 STACKED TIPS

The clues define words in increasing order of length that contain the same three letters at the beginning of the word as they do at the end. As mentioned in the question, each clue gives a full definition of the answer (e.g. 'Expert' = SOPRANO in the first clue), and a cryptic part of only the non-repeated part ('soprano' = S in the first clue):

18 TRANSFORMATIONS

The table at the top defines transformations on the original word, each of which results in an English word:

PALE	♣	PAIL – homophone
	♦	LEAP/PEAL – anagram
	♥	PAL –delete final letter
	♠	GALE/TALE – change first letter

These can then be read as instructions to transform each word:

DAMP ♥ DAM ♠ YAM ♦ MAY ♠ LAY ♣ LEI

EARTH ♦ HEART ♥ HEAR ♠ GEAR ♦ RAGE ♥ RAG

STUDY ♦ DUSTY ♥ DUST ♠ BUST ♥ BUS ♦ SUB

STAGE ♦ GATES ♥ GATE ♣ GAIT ♠ WAIT ♣ WEIGHT

YEARLY ♠ PEARLY ♥ PEARL ♥ PEAR ♣ PAIR ♠ HAIR

Which can then be paired with the clues, as required:

▶ Hawaiian garment = LEI
▶ Head covering = HAIR
▶ Heaviness = WEIGHT
▶ Sandwich = SUB
▶ Scrap of cloth = RAG

⑲ **VENN 3**

Left set: Common US coin denominations

Right set: Common UK coin denominations

Intersection: Common coins in denominations used in both the US and the UK

▶ Note that a 50 cent coin was used until relatively recently in the US, but is no longer in general circulation. Other coin denominations have been used historically, but are not in current usage

- -

- ▶ PROLONGSPLIVERE = LIVE, LONG and PROSPER
- ▶ THRONETWEEO = ONE, TWO and THREE
- ▶ LOBSTARRECLOCKK = LOCK, STOCK and BARREL
- ▶ HARDTRICKYOM = TOM, DICK and HARRY
- ▶ WARWILDROTICOBHEN = LION, WITCH and WARDROBE
- ▶ CARDPAROVERMINAROGOATTSI = PAVAROTTI, DOMINGO and CARRERAS
- ▶ APARTOARHOTMISSHOS = ATHOS, PORTHOS and ARAMIS
- ▶ SCRAPNOCKPLEAP = SNAP, CRACKLE and POP
- ▶ BRAMAROURBRINICEY = BARRY, ROBIN and MAURICE

(I) **ODD PAIR OUT I**

The odd pair out is antic and clone. The words can be paired in such a way that the insertion of a letter in the middle of each pair creates a new word. Of these letters, Y is the only one of these letters that is not a (true) vowel:

- ▶ THERE**A**BOUTS
- ▶ ADULT**E**RATED
- ▶ DETER**I**ORATE
- ▶ TRAMP**O**LINES
- ▶ PAST**E**URISER
- ▶ ANTIC**Y**CLONE

(2) **GRIDFILL I**

B	L	U	I
N	G	E	N
A	R	E	D
I	O	G	I
V	L	L	O
T	E	Y	W

3) TAKE A LETTER

In each case a single letter can be removed, and the remaining letters then rearranged, to make a second word of a similar meaning.

- ▶ PILFER - P = RIFLE
- ▶ BLABBER - R = BABBLE
- ▶ NOMINATE - A = MENTION
- ▶ ENQUIRED - N = QUERIED
- ▶ CLATTER - C = RATTLE
- ▶ TRIFLE - E = FLIRT
- ▶ BASTE - S = BEAT

This spells out 'PRANCES', from which the letter 'N' can be removed to make the word 'CAPERS', which just like in all of the cases above has a similar meaning to the original word. So the solution is 'N'.

4) WORD MAESTRO

They are meanings of Italian words, as obliquely hinted at by the word 'maestro' in the title, for which there are no direct single-word equivalents in English:

- ▶ Abbiocco
- ▶ Gattara
- ▶ Meriggiare
- ▶ Ciofeca

$\binom{5}{}$ POP SUMS I

The names of the artists most commonly associated with each song form anagrammatic equations, so the example can be converted as follows:

▶ Smalltown Boy *becomes* Bronski Beat = More Than In Love *becomes* Kate Robbins

...since 'Bronski Beat' is an anagram of 'Kate Robbins'.

All songs in this question were top 20 hit singles in the UK, but can also be looked up in an online search engine to find their original artists.

Using the same logic to rewrite the first question in the puzzle:

▶ One Week *becomes* Barenaked Ladies = Make It With You *becomes* Bread + _____

...so you are looking for a recording artist whose name, when combined with the letters in 'Bread', is an anagram of 'Barenaked Ladies', or in other words is an anagram of 'NAKELADIES'. Such an artist is Neil Sedaka, so you can pick any Neil Sedaka song to complete the first equation. So the following is a valid solution, for example:

▶ One Week = Make It With You + Laughter in the Rain

The second equation can also be rewritten similarly:

▶ Viva La Vida *becomes* Coldplay + Big Log *becomes* Robert Plant +

The First Picture Of You *becomes* Lotus Eaters

= Pure Morning *becomes* Placebo + Refugees *becomes* Tears +

_____ + _____

...so you are looking for two recording artists, whose names, once combined, form an anagram of 'COLDPLAYROBERTPLANTLOTUSEATERS' minus 'PLACEBOTEARS', or in other words two artists which together form an anagram of 'DLYORPLNTLOTUATERS'.

As can perhaps be seen from the starting letters of the anagram, the artist Dolly Parton can be extracted, leaving 'LTUTERS', which is itself an anagram of the artist Turtles. So to complete the equation, you need two songs – one by Dolly Parton, and one by Turtles. So a valid solution is:

▶ Viva La Vida + Big Log + The First Picture Of You = Pure Morning + Refugees + Jolene + Happy Together

(6) OLD AND NEW

The terms have to be paired to form a series of retronyms – these are neologisms for things that have been superseded or supplemented by other more modern versions of the item. Each term, when replaced by a synonym, can be combined with another to form such a neologism:

▶ Presumptuous + cut = forward slash (neologism created after the advent of the backslash)

- ▶ Dawdler + post = snail mail (neologism for regular post created after the advent of electronic mail)
- ▶ Speechless + movie = silent film (neologism for an early film without speech, after the advent of the talkie)
- ▶ Actual + racket sport = real tennis (neologism for traditional tennis created after the advent of lawn tennis)
- ▶ Standard + cooker = conventional oven (neologism created after the advent of the microwave oven)
- ▶ Unbending + match = straight marriage (neologism created after the advent of same-sex marriages)
- ▶ Morning + transmit = AM radio (neologism created after the advent of FM radio)
- ▶ Broadsheet + reserve = paper book (neologism created after the advent of e-books)
- ▶ Aural + axe = acoustic guitar (neologism created after the advent of the electric guitar)

(7) HUNT THE CHARACTER

The three hints for the first component are solved as follows:

- ▶ Supply free moralist as a prototype (8, 4) clues EARLIEST FORM ('free moralist' supplied as – anagrammed as – a word meaning 'prototype')
- ▶ AN is an 'article', and 'peculiarity' can mean 'oddity' – so the answer is 'AN ODDITY'

- ‘pe’ and ‘imittion’ are both words meaning ‘to copy’ that are missing an ‘a’ (‘ape’ and ‘imitation’), or in other words can be described whimsically as ‘NOT A COPY’

EARLIEST FORM, AN ODDITY and NOT A COPY are all clues to the answer AN ORIGINAL.

The cryptic clues making up the second component are solved like this:

- ‘Drink covering good cups?’ clues ALGEBRA: ale (drink) around g (good) + bra (cups?)
- ‘Record freeze falling short’ clues LOGIC: log (record) + ic(e) (freeze falling short)
- ‘Hardened skin around much of incision’ clues CALCULUS: callus (hardened skin) around cu(t) (much of incision)

ALGEBRA, LOGIC and CALCULUS are examples of MATHS.

The third component is solved as follows:

- Demon, taupe and notion are anagrams of words meaning ‘head’, plus an extra letter: dome + n, pate + u, onion + t, which spells out ‘nut’ – another word for ‘head’
- Case, hatch and shell can be preceded by ‘nut’ to make new terms
- Polish and cool clue ‘buff’ and ‘fan’, which are synonyms for ‘nut’ as e.g. in the phrase ‘I’m a sports nut/buff/fan’

Overall you now have AN ORIGINAL MATHS NUT, which is both a clue to and an anagram of ALAN MATHISON TURING.

VENN 4

Left set: Countries in the northern hemisphere

Right set: Countries in the southern hemisphere

Intersection: Countries that are in both the northern and southern hemispheres

(9) **ISOLATE**

(10) **CRYPTIC MOVIE CLUB**

► The Mummy Returns: ma (mummy), reversed (returns)
► Men In Black: crew (men) in sable (black)
► Half A Sixpence: tan = half of tanner (sixpence)
► The Sixth Sense: VI (the sixth) + nous (sense)
► Some Like It Hot: hidden (some) in 'liKE IT Hot'
► The Naked Gun: revolver (gun) without its 'clothing' (naked)
► A Life Less Ordinary: biog (a life (story)) less O (Ordinary)

TITLE FEATURES

They contain the titles of other noted movies:

- ▶ If (1968 movie directed by Lindsay Anderson)
- ▶ Heat (1995 movie directed by Michael Mann)
- ▶ Ray (2004 movie directed by Taylor Hackford)
- ▶ Ran (1985 movie directed by Akira Kurosawa)
- ▶ Z (1969 movie directed by Costa-Gavras)
- ▶ Babe (1995 movie directed by Chris Noonan)
- ▶ Argo (2012 movie directed by Ben Affleck)

(12) **GRIDFILL 2**

	W	E	N
P	R	A	V
C	I	T	Y
E	D	H	N
G	T	T	O
L	U	S	L

The words with the same meaning are WEN and CITY.

(13) **GLOBETROTTING 2**

The words represent journeys between pairs of the world's hundred busiest airports:

- ▶ MAD-DEN = MADRID-DENVER
- ▶ SEA-MAN = SEATTLE-MANCHESTER
- ▶ BOM-BOS = MUMBAI-BOSTON
- ▶ LAX-IST = LOS ANGELES-ISTANBUL
- ▶ HEL-LAS = HELSINKI-LAS VEGAS

Of these, BOM-BOS is the longest journey, at 12,239 km (7,605 miles), so is the 'longest' word.

(14) EVEN MORE TANGLED TRIOS

- ▶ CLAMOURRELYRY = LARRY, MOE and CURLY
- ▶ SHAMTIMERRRANUVIPL = HAMMER, ANVIL and STIRRUP
- ▶ BLEATTCOMATOUTCONE = BACON, LETTUCE and TOMATO
- ▶ LSMEARMADIGULLME = SMALL, MEDIUM and LARGE
- ▶ FEARWITHINRED = EARTH, WIND and FIRE
- ▶ SHINLIKEROOKNE = HOOK, LINE and SINKER
- ▶ BAGDOUGLODY = GOOD, BAD and UGLY
- ▶ PALTUTORAMAINEOBINSLESS = PLANES, TRAINS and AUTOMOBILES
- ▶ SLOGAILSQUIDID = SOLID, LIQUID and GAS

(15) VENN 5

Left set = Olympic athletic events competed in by men

Right set = Olympic athletic events competed in by women

Intersection = Olympic athletic events competed in by both men and women

16 APT PROPERTY

The sum of the alphabetical values of its vowels (5 + 21 + 1 + 9 + 15), and that of its consonants (17 + 20 + 14), both equal 51 – thus forming a beautiful EQUATION!

17 DIGITALLY ENHANCED JIGSAW

Each answer must be written phonetically using letter and digit pronunciations, as follows:

¹M	N	8	²B	³4
⁴O	⁵G	⁶3	9	N
G	⁷G	O	⁸D	6
⁹D	¹⁰K	9	¹¹V	¹²N
¹³M	A	C	8	E

Across:

1. Arise = Emanate (MN8)

2. Earlier = Before (B4)

4. S-shaped moulding = Ogee (OG)

7. Shortest lines between points = Geodesics (GOD6)

10. Dog = Canine (K9)

11. French river and department = Vienne (VN)

13. Waste away = Emaciate (MAC8)

Down

1. Pictogram = Emoji (MOG)

2. Not harmful = Benign (B9)

3. Scientific crime department = Forensics (4N6)

5. Horse = Gee-gee (GG)

6. An essential amino acid = Threonine (3O9)

8. Stray = Deviate (DV8)

9. What's seized in Latin = Diem (DM)

12. Whichever = Any (NE)

(18) ODD PAIR OUT 2

The odd words out are darkness and heavy. All the words form pairs which share an antonym (opposite), but all of the other pairs are also heteronyms (same spelling, but different pronunciations and meanings):

▶ Present (absent/receive)

▶ Sow (boar/reap)

▶ Does (bucks/undoes)

▶ Supply (demand/rigidly)

▶ Close (distant/open)

By contrast, the two meanings of light, as antonyms of darkness and heavy, are not heteronyms – both have the same pronunciation.

(19) POP SUMS 2

First notice that each left-hand side contains four artists, and each right-hand side contains only one artist. The theme here is four-word song titles that are themselves made up of four successive one-word song titles. Each artist on the left is therefore to be replaced by an appropriate one-word song that they are associated with, and when these words are combined it will create a song associated with the artist on the right.

In the example:

▶ Elvis Presley (Don't) + Coldplay (Talk) + Radiohead (Just) + Prince (Kiss) = Right Said Fred (Don't Talk Just Kiss)

The equations can then be solved like this:

▶ Spice Girls (Goodbye) + Olivia Newton-John (Sam) + Adele (Hello) + Kenny Ball & His Jazzmen (Samantha) = Cliff Richard (Goodbye Sam Hello Samantha)

▶ Ashford & Simpson (Solid) + Spandau Ballet (Gold) + Commodores (Easy) + Sweet (Action) = T. Rex (Solid Gold Easy Action)

All the songs were top 20 hit singles in the UK.

(20) ALPHABETIC EXTRACTION

There are three keys: 'car', 'house' and 'factory' which can be used to decode the letters on each key. Each key should be 'inserted' into the alphabet, as also suggested by the title, 'alphabetic extraction'.

You can then use the modified alphabet to extract text from each numbered key. For example, using the 'car' key you can read each numbered key as follows:

C	A	R	B	D	E	F	G	H	I	J	K	L
A	B	C	D	E	F	G	H	I	J	K	L	M

M	N	O	P	Q	S	T	U	V	W	X	Y	Z
N	O	P	Q	R	S	T	U	V	W	X	Y	Z

This decodes to Key 1 = VLOHQDLM, Key 2 = AUTOMOBILE and Key 3 = QFRESFLUF. Of these, only Key 2 = AUTOMOBILE makes sense, and also matches up with this being the 'car' key – so key 2 is the car key.

Using similar logic you can use the 'factory' key to deduce that 1 = WORKSHOP, thus identifying key 1 as the factory key, and you can use the 'house' key to deduce that 3 = RESIDENCE, meaning that key 3 is the house key.

(21) GRIDFILL 3

S	E	O	H	C	
A	L	B	I	A	S
H	C	U	L	O	S
T	A	S	D	N	A
T	I	P	E	R	I

(22) FIND THE ACTRESS

Each phrase is a clue to a six-letter word:

▶ Angled	FISHED
▶ Baby's shoe	BOOTEE
▶ Body louse	COOTIE
▶ Curbed	BITTED
▶ Mountainside basin (Scot)	CORRIE
▶ Punched	FISTED
▶ Scrounged (Aust)	BOTTED
▶ Soccer	FOOTIE
▶ Started up (a computer)	BOOTED
▶ To potter	FOOTLE
▶ To snuggle (Scot)	COORIE
▶ Town near Liverpool	BOOTLE
▶ Was of the correct size	FITTED

Once you have a few of the answers, you might spot that they are very similar, and further that you can build a word ladder:

CORRIE > COORIE > COOTIE > FOOTIE > FOOTLE > BOOTLE > BOOTEE > BOOTED > BOTTED > BITTED > FITTED > FISTED > FISHED

At this point you can now 'find the actress' – if you add an extra word to both the start and end of the word ladder you can now change CARRIE to FISHER in 14 steps.

So the solution is Carrie Fisher.

(23) CODED TRIBUTE

This puzzle requires use of a keyword cipher. This is based on Alan Turing, using his full name of ALAN MATHISON TURING. When expressed as a keyword cipher, this becomes a letter-to-letter conversion that looks like this:

A L N M T H I S O U R G B C D E F J K P Q V W X Y Z

A B C D E F G H I J K L M N O P Q R S T U V W X Y Z

The text given in the question can now be decoded to say:

Recognized as a FOUNDING FATHER of ARTIFICIAL INTELLIGENCE with creations such as the AUTOMATIC COMPUTING ENGINE among his works, this pioneer created the TURING MACHINE which became a landmark in its field.

His final research was entitled THE CHEMICAL BASIS OF MORPHOGENESIS (published in 1952) describing the way in which non-uniformity may arise naturally out of a homogeneous, uniform state.

Authors

The puzzles in this book were edited by Gareth Moore, who also wrote the hints and the solution explanations.

The following puzzle authors created all of the puzzles for this book:

ANTHONY PLUMB
Anthony Plumb is a school teacher, living in Lincolnshire, England. He has enjoyed puzzles all his life, and especially crosswords. He writes them for various UK publications, including *The Telegraph*, *The Financial Times* and *The Independent* newspapers.

DANIEL PEAKE
Daniel Peake is a quiz and puzzle constructor from Reading, England. Writing quizzes from the age of 10, he has worked on BBC shows including *Beat the Brain*, *Two Tribes* and *Only Connect*. He also recently constructed murder mystery cases for television. He specializes in wordplay-based puzzles.

DAVID MILLAR
David Millar is an American puzzle author with more than a decade of puzzle-writing under his belt, and whose puzzles have previously featured in both UK and World Puzzle Championships. He lives in Fort Worth, Texas.

GARETH MOORE

Gareth Moore is the author of over 75 books of puzzles for both children and adults, and the creator of the daily brain-training site, BrainedUp.com. He creates all types of puzzle, ranging from crosswords and other word puzzles through to sudoku and logic puzzles, and all the way on to complex dot-to-dot, and maze books. He also creates sticker books and other types of activity content, as well as optical illusions, quizzes and trivia books.

He has written several books of brain and memory training puzzles, exercises and tips, and frequently appears on TV and radio as both a brain-training and a puzzle expert. His puzzles also appear in apps, on websites, in magazines and in newspapers, as well as in board games. He is also a board member of both the World Puzzle Federation and the UK Puzzle Association.

GUY CAMPBELL

Guy Campbell is a writer and designer from London. Responsible for over 30 books, including *The Boy's Book of Survival*, he also writes puzzles for newspapers and magazines in the UK, Australia, India, Scandinavia and France. He is also a keen poker player, and writes quiz questions for both TV shows and for *Trivial Pursuit*.

LAURENCE MAY

Laurence May is a software developer and backgammon enthusiast who has been inventing logic puzzles since he became obsessed with sudoku in 2005. Laurence's creations are regularly published in the UK in both *The Times* and *Daily Mail* newspapers, and have been featured in puzzle magazines around the world. He lives in Buckinghamshire, England, with his wife, two teenage daughters and a tiny cockapoo.

MICK HODGKIN

Mick Hodgkin is a journalist and cryptic crossword compiler, writing under the handles of Morph and Micawber. As Mick Twister (@twitmericks), he writes news limericks on Twitter and is the author of *There Was an Old Geezer Called Caesar: A History of the World in Limericks* (Anova, 2013) and *There Once Was a Man With Six Wives: A Right Royal History in Limericks* (Pavilion, 2017).

MIKE TURNER

Mike Turner writes quiz questions and puzzles across all types of media. He is Senior Writer for the BBC Two lateral thinking show *Only Connect*, specializing in writing the connecting walls. He has also written questions for BBC quizzes *The Code* and *Decimate*. He also researches obscure facts for the BBC Radio 4 programme *The Museum of Curiosity*, writes a weekly puzzle for *The Radio Times* and has provided content for various quizzing and puzzle apps.

In front of the camera, Mike has won many TV quiz shows in the UK, including *15 to 1* and *The Weakest Link Champions League*.

PHILIP MARLOW

Philip Marlow has worked in television journalism and social research. He compiles cryptic and general knowledge crosswords for several national UK newspapers, including *The Telegraph*, *Financial Times* and *The Independent*, where his guises are Shamus, Sleuth and Hypnos. He sets questions for BBC TV quiz shows, including *Only Connect* and *University Challenge*.

RICHARD HEALD

Richard Heald is a mathematics graduate and IT worker who lives in South Yorkshire, England. He has been a long-time fan, and occasional setter, of puzzles and quizzes, and was a series semi-finalist on the UK TV quiz shows *Only Connect* and *Countdown*. He has a particular love of competitive crossword solving and has on several occasions been the annual champion of *The Observer* newspaper's Azed clue-writing competition (see www.andlit.org.uk). He also served for five years as clue judge for The Crossword Club.

ZOE WALKER

Zoe Walker is a professional puzzle editor, and has worked on a number of puzzle books. She holds an M.Phil in Philosophy from the University of Cambridge, which may explain her fondness for puzzles which require deep thinking.